A tribute to the healing instinct of the early American medicine men—and to the stamina of their patients.

DOCTORS OF THE AMERICAN FRONTIER

Richard Dunlop

When a frontier gunman's wrist was shattered by a bullet, he lost his arm to amputation. When cholera struck a wagon train, the survivors buried the dead along the trail. Nineteenth-century medicine was harsh and primitive, and when a doctor could not be reached, pioneers often died from the hunting-knife surgery of a friend or from a homemade cure.

Here, in all its color, is the story of frontier medicine. Thoroughly researched, yet written with a light and lively hand, this chronicle spins a yarn about the rough-and-tumble era of the pioneer West—the days of sodbuster surgeons, cowboy doctors, railroad sawbones, riverboat remedies, old wives' cures, and get-rich-quick quacks.

And here are the great men of wilderness medicine: Ephraim McDowell who ignored the shouts of a lynch mob in backwoods Kentucky while he

(*Continued on back flap*)

DOCTORS OF THE AMERICAN FRONTIER

BY RICHARD DUNLOP

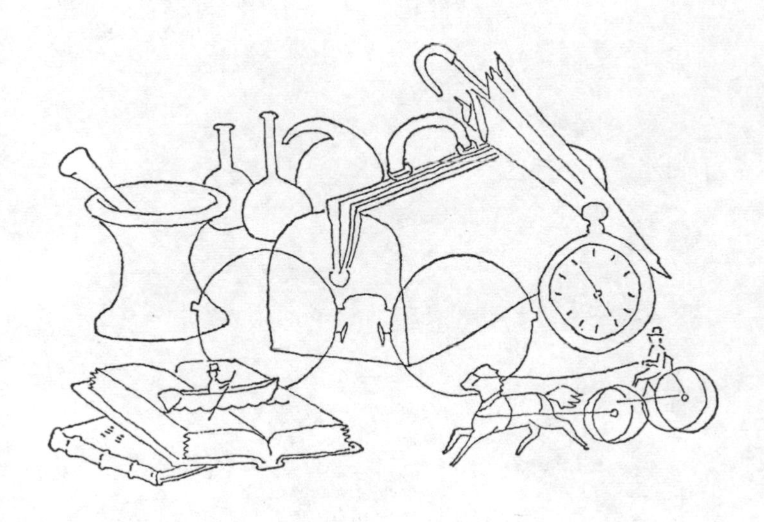

1965

DOUBLEDAY & COMPANY, INC., GARDEN CITY, NEW YORK

To the doctors of today
who honor in their own lives
the humanity and devotion
of the doctors of the American frontier

Library of Congress Catalog Card Number 65–13979

Printed in the United States of America
First Edition

ACKNOWLEDGMENTS

During the six years that I have researched *Doctors of the American Frontier*, I have been like a greenhorn venturing across the high plains and deserts of the frontier West. Often I never would have found my way to the next water hole if it had not been for the friendly natives of the region—librarians, scholars, bookmen, medical editors, aged doctors remembering the medicine of their youth, all who took time from their tasks to show me the way the trail ran.

The trail itself began at the Glen Ellyn, Illinois, home of Kenneth N. Anderson, editor of *Today's Health*, where the idea for the book was first discussed over lunch. Most of the chapters appeared in a periodical form in his magazine, which is published by the American Medical Association, and I'm indebted to the hundreds of the magazine's readers who wrote to me offering valuable research advice. In gathering information for the book I traveled over most of the western states, but the greatest sources for the book were libraries and museums in the Midwest and East. One of the first librarians to suggest the direction I might travel in my inquiries was Herman N. Henkel, librarian of the John Crerar Library in Chicago. His indefatigable Chief Medical and Scientific Librarian, Ella Salmonsen, proved of invaluable assistance in digging out significant references. Colton Storm of Chicago's Newberry Library made available fascinating publications and manuscripts, and Betty Baughman (now of the School of Library Service, University of California at Los Angeles) and Mary Jo Barten of the Chicago Historical Society Library opened their stacks to me. Mary Frances Rhymer, Curator of Prints at the Chicago Historical Society, helped with the illustration of the book.

Mrs. Susan Crawford, librarian of the Library of the American Medical Association in Chicago, was among the first librarians whom I consulted and among the last. Aubrey Gates, John Roch, and R. Roy Keaton of the A.M.A. staff opened up new paths of research. Kathleen Worst, of the Library of the American College of Surgeons in Chicago, turned up scores of books and periodicals for me to read. Dr. John Blake, Chief of the History of Medicine Section, the National Library of Medicine, Bethesda, Maryland, was my guide to his library's huge collection.

I found particularly useful books and documents at the Northwestern University Medical School Library in Chicago, the Deering Library on the campus of Northwestern University in Evanston, and the library of the University of Illinois Medical School in Chicago, but there were useful materials also in the Boston Public Library, the New York Public Library, and the Chicago Public Library. Alys Freeze, Head, Western History Department of the Denver Public Library, was also of great assistance to me.

Museum collections which helped to bring the medical practices of the westering frontier closer to me are in the St. Louis Medical Society's Bicentennial Medical Museum, the Howard Dittrick Museum of Historical Medicine at Cleveland, the Mariners Museum, Newport News, Virginia, and the Museum of Medical Progress, developed by the State Medical Society of Wisconsin at Prairie du Chien in the restored military hospital of old Fort Crawford, where Surgeon Beaumont made many of his remarkable studies of the human digestive system through the "window in the stomach" of Alexis St. Martin. Robert E. Ladd, Supervisor of the Tombstone Court House Historical Monument in Tombstone, Arizona, assisted me too.

Doctors who guided me along the frontier past of their profession included: O. O. Beck of Birmingham, Michigan; John C. Brougher of Vancouver, Washington; Howard C. Clark of Wichita, Kansas; Willard F. Goff of Seattle, Washington; C. A. Robins of Lewiston, Idaho; W. Andrew Bunten of Cheyenne, Wyoming; Carl P. Schlicke of Spokane, Washington; R. T. Whiteman of Cambridge, Idaho. Mrs. F. P. Ralston of Knoxville, Iowa, niece of the fascinating frontier military surgeon, Valentine McGillicuddy, helped me to learn about her uncle, and Mrs. Edith Fish of Berkeley, California, told me about her father, Dr. George Goodfellow, the gunfighter's surgeon of Tombstone, Arizona. Mrs. Henry S. Hiestand of Marietta, Pennsylvania, despite her ninety-two years of age, informed me about her father, the frontier military surgeon, Dr. Jenkins FitzGerald, and promised to stay alive to see my book into print. Such a plucky old lady is the worthy daughter of a frontier doctor.

Organized medicine, from the grass-roots county medical societies to the American Medical Association, also proved very co-operative. I particularly appreciate the assistance of: Oliver E. Ebel, Executive Director of the Kansas Medical Society in Topeka; J. P. Sanford, Executive Secretary of the Kentucky State Medical Association in Louisville; Vada L. Davis, Librarian of the Michigan State Medical Society in East Lansing; L. R. Hegland, Executive of the Montana Medical Association in Billings; Charles H. Crownhart, Executive Secretary, and Carol Cowan, Medical Reporter of the State Medical Society of Wisconsin in Madison; and Else Kolhede, Executive Secretary of the Wayne County Medical Society, Detroit. Medical editors, who have long scouted the trails along which they directed me, include: George X. Schoenlein, M.D., editor of the Cincinnati Journal of Medicine; Perry R. Ayres, M.D., editor of the Ohio Medical Journal in Columbus; Robert E. Van Demark, M.D., editor of the South Dakota Journal of Medicine in Sioux Falls; Mrs. Marilyn Baker, managing editor of the Texas State Journal of Medicine in Austin; and Leon Summit, editor of Pfizer Laboratories' *Spectrum* in New York City. Eugene H. Connor, M.D., of the School of Medicine, University of Louisville, pointed out valuable source materials concerning Ephraim McDowell and Daniel Drake, great pioneer Kentuckians. State historical societies in the West proved excellent sources too. Nyle Miller, Secretary, and Robert W. Richmond, Archivist, of the Kansas State Historical Society in Topeka; H. J. Swinney, Director of the Idaho Historical Society at Boise; and Richard Cropp, Assistant Secretary of the South Dakota

State Historical Society in Pierre, were among the people who made the book possible. Father Davis of the Society of Jesus; my own associate pastor, the Reverend George Kincheloe of the First Presbyterian Church of Arlington Heights, Illinois; and William B. Miller, Manager of the Presbyterian Historical Society in Philadelphia, assisted me in my study of Dr. Marcus Whitman. I'm indebted also to Dr. Gene M. Gressley, Director of the Western History and Archives Department of the University of Wyoming library in Laramie; to Dorman H. Winfrey, Archivist of the Library of the University of Texas in Austin; and to C. L. Sonnichsen, Dean of Texas Western College at El Paso. Bill Lynde of El Paso, a long-time western friend and fellow student of the western frontier, Louise Shadduck, Secretary of the State of Idaho's Department of Commerce and Development, and Cattie Lou Miller, Commissioner of Public Information of the State of Kentucky, all assisted me along the way. So did such railroad men as Joel Priest and Ed Schafer of the Union Pacific, H. F. Compton of the Northern Pacific, Bill Burk of the Santa Fe, and Chester C. Guy, M.D., of the Executive Board of the American Association of Railway Surgeons.

Above all, I'm indebted to my fellow members of the Chicago Corral of the Westerners, who over the years have encouraged my scholarship while condemning my errors. Don Russell, author and editor, Leland Case, editorial adviser to the Methodist Publishing Company, and Dr. John Gray, professor in the Northwestern University Medical School, were singularly helpful in these respects. I owe a particularly huge debt to Franklin Meine, Westerner of the Chicago corral, editor, folklorist, historian, and fellow trailer along the paths of frontier history, whose own work has been both a model and an inspiration to me. Last of all, I am grateful to my family doctor, Earl Stephenson, for his selfless service in suburbia and among nearby Mexican migrant workers, and to an understanding wife, who has done all the usual things that a writer's wife is heir to, and much more. These and many others have helped me along the trail.

CONTENTS

LIST OF ILLUSTRATIONS

DOCTORS OF THE AMERICAN FRONTIER

Chapter I

MEDICINE AND THE FRONTIER

The typical nineteenth-century American frontiersman was wan with fever, gaunt, and spindle-shanked. His wife was scrawny and peaked; their children were sick and fretful.

"Death is their doctor, and the grave their hospital," observed Dr. Daniel Darling, a frontier physician in the old Northwest in 1842.

The backwoodsmen of the Ohio forests, the boatmen of the Mississippi Valley, the mountain men and explorers beyond the Missouri, the trailers of western trails, the miners of the Far West, Indian fighters, ranchers, and sodbusters, all often lived hundreds of miles from the nearest doctor. It was a hard-scrabble life. In the forests people existed in log huts with clapboard roofs, clay chimneys, and puncheon floors on which they sat if a box or stool were not handy and slept if there were no pole-frame bed. They dwelled in sod huts on the plains, jerry-built mining camps in the western mountains, and if they wore army uniforms, they dwelled in ill-ventilated forts which were better constructed to repel Indians than the incursions of disease.

Fleas and bedbugs made nightly sallies from their nests in the cracks and chinks of frontier dwellings.

"Nothing but hell fire and brimstone would remove them," noted Dr. A. B. Palmer, who practiced in backwoods Michigan. "We dared not resort to that extreme remedy for fear of burning the castle."

Pioneers settled close to streams when they could and were pestered by flies and gnats by day and mosquitoes by night. Malarial and typo-malarial fevers sapped their strength. Nobody suspected the role insects played in spreading them. Families ate from a common platter and drank from a common tin cup. Cookie in the lumber camps and on ranch roundups and a pioneer mother alike served up nearly indigestible foods from greasy frying pans. The frontiersman's hungry gluttony for half-baked hot bread and his fondness for fiery country whiskey further burdened his digestion. Severe indigestion and dysentery were common. Western miners and soldiers in garrison virtually subsisted on dried and salted meat. Vegetables and fruits were scarce, and scurvy raged. Trees fell on settlers and on loggers; rocks rolled on placer miners working river bottoms. The bona fide western frontier was truly wild, and stabs and gunshot wounds were frequent.

The Frenchman Alexis de Tocqueville, who traveled the America of the 1840s, wrote that to go from east to west was to go backward in time. The doctor who rode west rode backward in time too. He slept on the ground when he could to avoid flea-infested cabins and inns where a dozen men were customarily lodged in a room with three or four in each bed. He crunched through winter forests on snowshoes, forded swollen rivers on his horse in the spring, and rode sweating down the hot trails of summer. Often the only drugstore in hundreds of miles was in his saddlebag. He pounded his own drugs, made tinctures and infusions, and put up presciptions with the aid of horn balances and a china mortar.

At the end of a long and wearisome ride, the doctor set broken limbs, bound up wounds and injuries, delivered babies, fought smallpox, pneumonia, and diphtheria. His cures were blunt. He slit the throat of a child choking with diphtheria and opened the windpipe. He kept the aperture from closing with fishhooks. A frontier doctor's cures were vigorous too. Seizing a patient sick with fever, the doctor opened a vein and drew blood until unconsciousness was near. This lowered the heart action. The patient broke into perspiration. His fever and delirium vanished. The doctor next administered tartar as an emetic and followed it with a calomel purge. Finally he "locked the bowels," as the expression went, with opium. When the doctor paid a return visit, the patient usually declared himself "well, if a little weak," most likely to prevent additional treatment. The doctor was ingenuous too. If a man broke his leg, he reduced the fracture and tied rough-hewn shingles on each side of the break. To keep the leg pulled straight, he constructed a traction apparatus with a rope and a flatiron or a few horseshoes.

Many of a frontier doctor's methods sound curious today, not just because he was improvising in the wilderness but because he was a prisoner of the medical thought of his time. Bloodletting and cupping were still widespread in the first half of the century on both sides of the Atlantic. The germ theory was only sketchily understood by a few medical leaders, although most doctors were at least disposed to the use of soap and water. There were no tablets, no pills, and no fluid extracts. There were no hypodermics, and a doctor rubbed a quantity of morphine or opium into a scratch in the skin to relax his patient. Some doctors carried a little wooden box with a drum in it which served as a crude stethoscope, but most preferred to place an ear against the patient's chest to listen to his heart.

The nineteenth century was a creative era in world medicine. In England, while American frontiersmen were pressing steadily westward, Sir Charles Bell studied the anatomy of the nervous system and determined that there were two kinds of nerves, sensory and motor. Richard Bright traced dropsy to its origin in diseased kidneys, and Thomas Addison learned about anemia. The German Hermann von Helmholtz invented the ophthalmoscope, looked through it, and first saw the fundus of the living eye; the Frenchman Louis Pasteur advanced from the study of why wines soured to the pasteurization of milk and the prevention of rabies. Joseph Lister in England pioneered antiseptic surgery, and Crawford W. Long in America introduced ether anesthesia.

Great medical scientists even arose in the dark forests of the American frontier. Ephraim McDowell in backwoods Kentucky braved a lynch mob and performed the first ovariectomy in medical history, and at a Great Lakes military outpost Surgeon William Beaumont studied human digestion through a hole torn by a shotgun blast in the stomach of a young voyageur. Daniel Drake explored the interior wilderness of North America mapping diseases and their causes and consequences in the lives of the inhabitants and created a masterpiece of medical geography.

Year by year the giants of medicine expanded knowledge, but even in Europe and on the eastern seaboard of America the common practitioner lagged decades behind them. Most medical schools still undertook to award a doctor his sheepskin in one year; some offered a two-year course. It was not until 1871 that Harvard lengthened its course of study to three years. Diploma mills were numerous, and because a doctor held a degree did not necessarily mean he was fit to practice.

Most frontier doctors never saw the inside of a medical school. They were educated through a medical apprenticeship, which was right out of the Middle Ages. A young apprentice ground powders, mixed pills, and rode with the doctor on his rounds. He held the basin for his preceptor when he bled a patient; he adjusted plasters and learned to sew up wounds by watching the doctor at work. In between his medical studies, he swept out the office, cleaned the doctor's empty bottles and jars, and tended the night bell. A few doctors learned from books alone. Dr. Henry B. Roland, a pioneer physician in Indiana, "read" his profession while locked up in a jail because he was unable to pay his debts.

On the frontier a doctor was ranked with the schoolmaster, the minister and the judge. When he rode out to see the sick, boys lifted their hats to him and girls curtsied. In many parts of the West even the settlers' vicious dogs were not allowed to snap at the doctor as he cantered by. The physician was conceded the right to shoot a dog if he proved a nuisance. In the Far West bandits and rustlers let the doctor ride by unharmed. After all, a man never knew when he might desperately need his services.

Being one of the few educated men in a frontier community, the doctor was called upon to help make the laws, to preside at kangaroo courts, and to teach morals to the young. In some places he was also in demand to read to young and old the latest tales of Sir Walter Scott or the adventurous fiction then the staple of

The Saturday Evening Post. His travels made the doctor a peripatetic newspaper.

All of this did not mean that the pioneer doctor was universally honored on the frontier, for there were many frontiersmen who hated him simply because he was an educated man. Some sniggered and repeated the popular saying, "The boy who goes into medicine is too lazy for farm or shop, too stupid for the bar, and too immoral for the pulpit." Others held all doctors in contempt because of the miserable treatment they had received at the hands of quacks, who far outnumbered actual physicians.

On the frontier anyone claiming to be a physician or surgeon could practice. It was not until 1874 that New York regulated medical practice. In 1875 Nevada became the first frontier state to pass a medical-practice law, and California followed in 1876. But even though most other western states and territories adopted such laws by the end of the nineteenth century, they were only spasmodically enforced. Pioneers paid less attention to whether a man had a degree or a license to practice than to the cures he managed.

There were "yarb and root" doctors, including strange white medicine men, who had been captured as children by Indians and brought up in Indian villages. The sheepskin doctor from an eastern college learned much from these irregulars, and over sixty of the herbs they used are now listed in the modern pharmacopoeia. But there were also snake-oil doctors, *ersatz* faith healers, and charlatans in stovepipe hats who effected all their cures with a secret remedy. Ignorant frontiersmen almost seemed to prefer quacks and their cures.

"When one of these quackeries is innoculated into a community," complained Dr. Daniel Drake, "nothing can arrest its spred or limit its duration. Every dog has his day, and so has every nostrum."

At the time of the Civil War, quackery on the frontier took on new vigor. The manufacturers of patent medicine, as yet unchallenged by the infant American Medical Association and untrammeled by a Pure Food and Drug Act, flooded the nation as a whole and the West in particular with bitter syrups and ointments. Spirometers, vaporizers, electric batteries, and a myriad of cure-alls were sold to combat what the ads in frontier newspapers called "hacking coughs," "paling cheeks," and "wasting manhood." Historian Arthur Schlesinger, remarking on this episode in the country's medical history, pays a tribute to the robustness of Americans. He maintains that a less sturdy nation might have been exterminated. Perhaps so, but on the frontier, doctors found that along with the diseases and accidents of pioneer life they now also had to treat the victims of patent medicines.

Physicians angrily denounced eastern manufacturers and frontier charlatans. Spread thin as they were over the far-flung frontier, the doctors traveled long distances to meet and form county and state medical associations in order to combat quackery. They also quarreled among themselves as to the right medical discipline to follow. All over Europe and America nineteenth-century medicine was shaken by contending schools. On the American frontier where nerves easily rubbed raw, doctors sometimes settled their medical differences at pistol point. Dr. Benjamin Winslow Dudley, one of the greatest of Kentucky frontier physicians, once cut another doctor's femoral artery with a well-placed pistol shot. He instantly ligated the vessel and saved his professional enemy's life. The two doctors shook hands and became fast friends.

The middle decades of the century were turning points in world medicine, and even on the remote frontier doctors became familiar with Pasteur's findings and Lord Lister's work. By 1871 carbolic acid was used widely to kill germs. By 1875 frontier surgeons were bravely cutting their way into the abdomens of victims of gunfire or appendicitis. By 1881 the wasting fevers of the frontier had been broken down into two separate diseases, malaria and typhus, with two different if still mysterious causes. Diphtheria was isolated as a specific throat disease. Doctors on the frontier now used anesthesia when they had it; otherwise they still filled their patients with whiskey before they cut into them. Dr. Lewis J. Moorman, who practiced in Oklahoma, explained that if "they can get drunk and shoot one another up, they can be sewed up without drugs."

Most of the diseases common on the early frontier were still virulent during the last fifty years before the U. S. Census Bureau officially announced in 1893 that the frontier was closed. Summer sickness wasted sodbusters' children on the Great Plains just as it had the young of the settlers of Mississippi Valley forests. Mountain fever was still inexplicable, and nobody surmised that Rocky Mountain spotted fever was transmitted by ticks. Some diseases, unheard of in the Far West when the first mountain men and military explorers entered the region, were now common. Smallpox, chicken pox, and measles swept with deadly virulence over the Indian tribes soon after their contact with white parties. They decimated pioneers too. Beginning in the 1840s cholera slipped up the rivers from New Orleans on river steamers and marched over the overland trails with covered-wagon trains. All a doctor could do was to spoon red pepper mixed in whiskey into the dying. When a cholera victim was dead, his fellows buried him by the trail. Often the next westward-bound wagon train camped on the graves of the last.

Doctors on the frontier fought Indians, built cabins and roads, and also wrote reports on meteorology and anthropology. They searched the woods and prairies for herbal substitutes for hard-to-get eastern drugs. Between their grueling rides to succor the sick and injured, some of them built laboratories and tried to advance the sum of medical knowledge. They argued for sewage disposal, tried to regulate bawdyhouses, and denounced heavy drinking and the sale of tainted meat. In California mining camps they attempted to stamp out opium smoking among the Chinese. Ranchers and sodbusters cursed doctors who insisted that they abandon wells tainted with typhoid. They resented the doctors' demand that families sick with communicable disease be quarantined. It was not neighborly to let those nice folks down the road suffer with diphtheria without stopping by to bring them a cake and a little sympathy. The doctor had no heart.

Military surgeons and civilian doctors alike, graduates of medical schools and irregular physicians too brought the art of healing to the western wilderness. They lived lives of derring-do, of hardship lightened more by humor than by bravery, of sacrifice, and mainly of poverty which their spirit of service transformed into riches. Even as they helped to push back the frontiers of the continent, they pushed back the frontiers of man's medical knowledge.

Chapter II

HUNTING-KNIFE SURGERY

They called him a mountain man, and he was a two-legged cousin to a grizzly bear, except that he was more ornery. Once, as he trapped beaver in the lonely mountains, an Indian bullet smashed his leg. He should have died because there was no companion to help him, but he wrapped a tourniquet of buckskin thongs around his thigh and amputated with a hunting knife. He clamped off the bleeding arteries with a bullet mold. He whittled himself a leg of hickory.

Months later, when he stomped into a frontier saloon, the men at the bar named him "Pegleg" Smith. Pegleg on one leg was still to be reckoned with. One night in an Independence barroom he drank so much the grizzly came out in him. The boys shoved him out of doors and locked the door. Cursing, he blew the lock off with his gun and charged into a poker game. All four players opened fire on the berserk mountain man. Pegleg's gun was empty. He jerked off his hickory leg, whirled it around and struck out the candles. He swung his leg at his enemies in the dark, killing two, and knocking one senseless. As he lunged for the door, he shot the fourth with a gun he had taken from a fallen adversary. Pegleg Smith's do-it-yourself surgery had to be judged an unqualified success.

During the first part of the nineteenth century fashionable men in Europe and on the eastern seaboard decked themselves out in beaver hats. French voyageurs paddled up the northern rivers to trap the beaver to satisfy the demand for pelts. Anglo-American trappers went up the Missouri and other rivers into the Rocky Mountains where beaver were also plentiful. Known as mountain men, they lived much of their lives alone or in small parties hundreds of miles from doctors. Their school of do-it-yourself medicine was as rough-and-ready as their tumultuous yearly rendezvous on the Green River. Whiskey was the king of all remedies—proof against the common cold, rheumatism, and boredom. From Indian medicine men these half-savage whites learned about herb teas, poultices, and sweat baths, but they put their faith in whiskey and drained their jugs even as they applied Indian cures. Whiskey was the only anesthetic too. Before a wounded man submitted to the hunting knife surgery of a companion, he drank his fill.

Pegleg was not the only mountain man called Smith. There was also gentlemanly Jedediah, who carried with him a book on the Lewis and Clark expedition given to him by his family doctor back East when he was a twelve-year-old. Jedediah could quote Shakespeare and discourse about the Bible with the insight of a theologian, but he was a mountain man through and through. When he led a party of trappers into the dry lands west of the White River of South Dakota, two men fainted from loss of water. He buried them in the sand up to their necks in order to keep their bodies from drying out. Forging ahead, he found a water hole, filled his canteen, and returned to trickle the life-restoring liquid through the dying men's parched lips. Later he used the same method to save lives in the deserts of Nevada and Utah.

'Diah's mild manners hid a grizzly in him, too, or he never would have lived to tell of his encounter with a real bear. As he led a party of trappers through the Black Hills, he rounded a rock and was seized by a huge grizzly. The beast clamped his head in its teeth, broke several of his ribs with its embrace, and threw him to the ground before his comrades could kill it. Young James Clyman later wrote about treating his leader's wounds on the spot.

"I asked the Captain what was best. He said 'one or two for water and if you have a needle and thread get it out and sew up my wounds around my head' which was bleeding freely. I got a pair of scissors and cut off his hair and then began my first job of dressing wounds."

Examining Smith, Clyman found the bear had taken nearly all his head in its enormous mouth. The wound extended from close to his left eye on one side to close to his right ear on the other. The skull was laid bare to "the crown of the head leaving a white streak where his teeth passed."

One of Smith's ears was torn from his head out to the outer rim.

"After stitching on the other wounds in the best way I was capable and according to the Captain's directions," said Clyman, "the ear being the last, I told him I could do nothing for his ear."

"Oh, you must try to stitch it up some way or other," said Smith.

Clyman stitched the ear through and through, over and over, matching the lacerated parts together as he sewed. After Clyman was finished, Smith mounted his horse and rode to camp. He kept his ear.

Old Hugh Glass proved even harder to kill. Up Grand River a grizzly mother flung him to the ground and tore chunks out of his leg. As he screamed in pain, she tenderly offered the flesh to her cubs. Then she attacked again, grinding her teeth into his shoulders. Other members of the party came up at this moment and killed the bear. The blood-soaked old man rolled in agony on the ground. His companions made a bed of robes and blankets and placed him on it.

Usually mountain men carried a wounded man with them. They tied him to his saddle or transported him in a travois dragged behind a horse. Sometimes they cut two flexible poles about twenty-four feet long and placed them on the ground three feet apart. Spreading a buffalo robe between the poles, they fastened it to each side. This made a six-foot swinging hammock with shafts protruding six feet at each end, which could be attached to the saddles of a pair of horses. It seemed impossible to move Hugh Glass, so a man and a boy stayed behind to watch over him until he died. They fed him soup, dressed his wounds with cold water, and kept the stinging flies away. For all their savage ways, mountain men were faithful to their friends; but when a party of hostile Indians appeared in the neighborhood, the man and boy deserted Hugh, who seemed certain to die within a few hours at the most. Instead of dying, Hugh Glass regained consciousness. He cursed the men who had left him to his lonely fate and washed his wounds. Making only a few hundred yards a day, he crawled on his hands and knees more than a hundred miles to Fort Kiowa on the Missouri.

Since bears were the most dangerous opponents the mountain men encountered in the wilderness, it is not surprising that Dr. William Frazier Tolmie saw fit to include a way to defeat them among botanical and clinical notes he made in his journal. Dr. Tolmie, surgeon and naturalist, who, looking for herbs, made the first ascent of Mount Rainier, came ashore from a ship that reached the Pacific Northwest and met a trapper named Mackay.

"Mackay has had many encounters with the bear," he wrote, "and the best way he says when a wounded bear rushes at you is to stand and reload and when he comes near if your gun is unloaded look at him steadily and he will not attack but raise on his hind legs, will continue to return your gaze until tired of his position when he betakes himself quietly off."

Dr. Murray L. Johnson, a modern-day physician, in passing on this prescription against bears, dryly adds, "We have his journal, so apparently the author did not have any opportunity for testing this theory."

Indians inflicted their share of wounds on the mountain men too. Both redskins and whites were adept at a simple operation, in which they cut a circle around a dead man's crown and then neatly yanked off his scalp—so adept, in fact, that Jim Bridger's constant advice to his friends was: "Keep your scalps by thinking of them."

To end up beneath a scalping knife was bitter, but it was often preferable to being seriously wounded far from any medical help. A Blackfoot brave shot Kit Carson in the neck and shoulder during a pitched battle with a party of trappers. The mountain men took cover behind a knoll. They stuffed beaver fur against Kit's wound to stop the bleeding and bound it in place with a strap of buckskin cut from his coat. The bandage did not stop the blood, and Kit would have bled to death by dawn except that the night was so cold it capped the wound with gory ice.

Carson was one of the most expert hunting-knife surgeons in the mountains. When John C. Frémont brought twelve-year-old Randolph Benton, son of the senator, on one of his expeditions, Kit, who guided the explorers, taught the boy how to extract an arrow from a wound. He showed him how to push it on through the body and cut off the iron-barbed head. The naked shaft could then be withdrawn. If this maneuver proved impossible, then there was nothing left to do but to wait until the body softened the sinews which fastened the arrowhead to the shaft. Then the shaft could be pulled free and the head dug out with a knife.

Mountain men seemed to be too tough for disease. Fur trader William Ashley said that they suffered only from "slight fevers produced by colds or rheumatic affections, contracted while in the discharge of guard duty on cold and inclement nights." He added that in the four years of one of his greatest fur-gathering expeditions in the Far West he did not lose a "single man by death except those who came to their end prematurely by being either shot or drowned." Probably the trappers' camps were so remote that contagion spared them. Cholera, which later was epidemic on western trails, had not yet spread into the wilds. Even smallpox, which raged along the westering frontier and decimated whole Indian tribes, passed over the mountain men.

Strenuous measures were taken to combat the illness that did appear. Alexander Henry, a far-ranging fur trader, led his men to the Red River of the North, where one of them suffered from colic. Henry, who apparently possessed a complete arsenal of remedies, says:

"I gave him some essence of peppermint, but it did not cure him; soon after gave him some sweet oil, which he threw up. He was in great pain. I gave him a dose of jalap, which he soon threw up, and his pain increased. I then gave him an extraordinary dose of Glauber's salts, which after some time took its course, but it did not appear to relieve him much."

Nineteenth-century doctors often gave as a cathartic the powdered root of the Mexican jalap plant and the sodium-sulfate compound named for the German physician Johann Glauber, but not in such heavy doses.

The next day the redoubtable amateur physician gave the sick man another powerful emetic which proved effective. Henry had an equally stern cure for a split thumb.

"One of my men split his thumb with an ax in a shocking manner," he wrote, "and having neglected it, the wound was in a sad condition. I washed it with sal ammoniac until it bled, when the poor fellow was dancing with pain and swore he would rather have it cut off."

Henry rubbed wine and gunpowder on itching skin and treated chilblains and pneumonia with the benzoin resin called Turlington's Balsam. But when it comes to providing rigorous treatment he could not compete with the Cheyenne medicine man who treated William Bent of Bent's Fort for a throat infection which threatened to choke him to death. The medicine man strung a sinew with sandburs and dipped it into hot buffalo tallow. This he forced down Bent's throat with a peeled stick. When the tallow melted, he jerked the string out, pulling the infected membrane with it. Bent survived.

If a mountain man suffered from urinary retention, he made a catheter of willow bark and relieved himself. He had far more difficulty with a toothache. John Smith, trapping on the upper Missouri, was struck by a terrible toothache that twisted his face with neuralgia. He was at least twenty-five hundred miles from a dentist. In agony he floated down the river in a bullboat to Fort McKenzie. He pounded on the gate.

"Let me in," he howled. "I got a terrible toothache. I want something to kill the pain."

The storekeeper at the fort knew when he had the upper hand. He demanded almost all the trapper's furs for a bottle of laudanum. The desperate Smith agreed. He climbed in his nearly empty boat and started down the river, taking an occasional tug on his precious pain-quenching bottle. As he camped that night, Indians closed in, took all his remaining possessions, slit his boat, and sank it. He scarcely noticed what they did since they left him his bottle. He nipped at it to deaden the excruciating pain in his jaw. Finally the Indians demanded that they too should enjoy a few pulls on the strange bottle which made the white so oblivious to their deviltry. After a few slugs of laudanum, the Indians keeled over. Smith snatched back the bottle, broke their bows, and helped himself to their powder, lead, and buffalo robes. He captured a pony and rode away.

Lice were another common affliction, which mountain men carried away with them from their amorous visits to Indian villages. Dr. Tolmie described a visit from several Indian women who squatted on their hips around his fire and "commenced a war of extermination against the creeping things in each other's heads, each when she made a prize, adroitly placing it on the tip of her tongue and then with the incisors giving the coup de grace."

Kit Carson had a less tasty way of ridding himself of lice. He slipped off his clothes and tossed them into a nest of huge red ants. Then he went for a swim in the river until the ants had eaten the graybacks.

A mountain man did not eat his lice in Indian style, but this was not because he was squeamish about his diet. Joe Meek stuck his hands into anthills and licked the ants from his fingers. He savored crisp fried crickets, and if on a long ride he ran short of provisions, he drew blood from his horse's ears to give sustenance to his soup. Mountain men substituted cherry-root tea for coffee and ate breadroot sliced thin and sprinkled with gunpowder in place of salt. They munched on wild roots and greens. Ashley writes that fresh meat was their principal diet. This meant as pioneer doctor Lewis J. Moorman said: "Panther meat, then beaver tails boiled, unborn buffalo calves before they hair over, rattlesnakes like a long chicken neck only thinner, skunks and goats. Then there is buffalo. I mean the whole critter, mind you, barring hide, hair, horns and hoofs. Red muscle meat will do you in the settlements, maybe, or where you can get plenty of greens and vegetables. But on the prairie you will have the cows' insides for choice marrow, lights, heart and tongue, warm liver spiced with gall and best of all, guts—plain guts—and raw at that."

The mountain men thrived on such a diet. They roamed a wilderness and made it their own. Then the wagon trains began to push into their land of high prairies, tumbled mountains and scorched desert. The mountain men lingered on, not knowing that they and their way of life were already history. In 1867, old Kit Carson lay dying at Fort Lyon on the upper Arkansas. A few years before he had been thrown and dragged by his horse on a hunting trip and hurt internally. Army Surgeon Tilton helped him to a bed of buffalo robes and prescribed a light diet and no tobacco. On May 23 the old mountain man cocked an eye at the cook.

"Cook me some first-rate doin's—a buffalo steak and a bowl of coffee and a pipe are what I need," he said.

The doctor objected, but Kit seared the air with some carefully stored up oaths. The frightened cook whomped up a mountain man's robust meal. Kit ate with appetite and called for his pipe, not a fancy store pipe but an old clay pipe given to him by an Indian long ago. He smoked and told stories of the high mountains in the old times. He coughed as he yarned, and hemorrhaged; a violent aneurism ruptured into his trachea.

"I'm gone! Doctor, *compadre, adios!*" he cried.

Kit Carson, who had spent a healthy lifetime in the wilderness remote from medical science, died with a doctor at his side.

Chapter III

DEATH IN THE WOMB

Ephraim McDowell listened to the messenger's strange story of a woman laboring through her ninth and tenth months in a wilderness cabin. Two doctors already in attendance were baffled. Would Dr. McDowell come? He checked the bottles in the pouches of his saddlebag, drew on his rough coat, and rode away from Danville, which in 1809 was the principal town of the Kentucky frontier.

Sixty miles later, his worn saddlebags rubbing against his long legs, he jogged into Motley's Glen. Thin blue smoke curling from the chimney of the cabin meant a cozy fire and a place on the puncheon floor where he could stretch out in his blankets. But first he had a baby to deliver.

There was snow on the ground, but behind the cabin a small stream was purling over the stones in its bed. A half-grown boy dipping a bucket of water from the brook stared at the tall doctor in the black slouch hat, black silk tie, and ruffled linen.

"How is your mother?" the doctor asked. He usually yarned and joked with children. He told firsthand tales of fishing, hunting, and Indian fighting for he had been raised on the frontier. Today he handed the reins to the boy and went inside the cabin.

"McDowell, it's good you're here," cried one of the waiting doctors. "We'll have to deliver the child at once."

McDowell's black eyes flicked past him to take in the rest of the room—the oiled-paper window, the powder horn, the enormous kettle on the fire, the Bible which had long ago come from Scotland, the two doctors, the covey of small children cringing in a corner, and the stocky woman, lying on her side on a narrow bed against one wall. Jane Crawford's features were too heavy;

her brown hair was unkempt; but her gray eyes glowed as she watched the doctor.

McDowell stepped to her side and without a word began his examination. As his gaunt fingers gently bared the mother's swollen abdomen, he began to tell an old Scotch tale, not to the woman but to the cowering children. His voice trailed on, and the white-faced children listened. His fingers searched Jane Crawford for the trouble she carried within her.

"No woman has ever recovered from what ails you," he finally said in a tired voice. "I can't tell you different and be honest. But if God wills it, you may not die."

Jane Crawford's face was ugly with pain; but to Dr. McDowell it had the frightening beauty of death.

"My poor babies," she said.

"The woman must be made to deliver the child," said one of the doctors.

"The woman has no child," said McDowell. "Her womb is empty. She carries an ovarian tumor."

Strange how his life had come to a sharp focus in this lonely cabin where a woman suffered. He believed in his Scotch Presbyterian heart that he had been predestined to this time and place since the day he was born in frontier Rockbridge County, Virginia, thirty-eight years before. His father had the frontiersman's westering instinct, and when Ephraim was twelve years old he took him over the Wilderness Trail to the dark and bloody land where there were Indians to fight, forest to be cleared, and cabins to be built. At the end of the trail was Danville, a village of 150 pioneers, who made Ephraim's father their judge.

Judge McDowell led the militia against the Indians, opposed the Aaron Burr faction which was conniving with the Spanish to detach the West from the Union, and raised his boy to be God-fearing and self-reliant. Ephraim preferred to read the books his father had brought from Virginia to playing with other boys and preferred exploring the unknown forest to reading books. He became a hunter worthy of his father. Carving his kill, he learned a dexterity with a knife which in future years would save lives.

When Ephraim grew tall with black eyes and a craggy face more purposeful than handsome, he rode east over the Wilderness Trail to Staunton, Virginia. His medical training began there in the office of Dr. Alexander Humphreys, one of the finest surgeons of his day. In 1793 he made the long voyage to Scotland, where at the University of Edinburgh the greatest medical faculty of the century had gathered. The lectures in internal medicine seemed dull to the young backwoodsman, but he worked hard in chemistry, anatomy, and surgery.

The judge could send little money to his son, and Ephraim was shabby and hungry. One day a blustering Irish runner making a Scotch tour arrived at Edinburgh and challenged the students to a race. American Ephraim McDowell stepped forth to save the honor of Scotland in a sixty-yard match. Bets mounted. McDowell let the Irishman win and then demanded a return engagement. Wagering every guinea he had on winning, he ran as if tomahawk-wielding Indians were on his heels. He beat his opponent and collected a large sum at odds of a hundred to one. His winnings paid his medical-school expenses. John Bell, renowned for his work on blood vessels, saw promise in the canny young American and gave him entree to the university's most exalted medical circles.

It was now fifteen years and half a world away from those earnest night discussions while the Scotch city slept around the learned doctors and their students. In the pioneer cabin in Motley's Glen Dr. McDowell brooded before the fire. Surgeons dressed wounds, cared for broken bones and sprains, amputated, took out kidney stones, repaired ruptures, and performed tracheotomies, but no doctor anywhere had ever attempted to remove an ovarian tumor. Not even John Bell had dared to cut into the abdominal cavity. Medical authorities said the foul air would infect the wound. Death would follow. If in the operating room of a medical school it was foolhardy to perform such an operation, here in the frontier forest with only the rudest instruments it would be deadly. Yet he remembered there had been surgeons at Edinburgh who wondered if a stricken woman might recover if only the tumor could be cut out of her womb.

McDowell turned from the fire to meet his patient's eyes. The woman could live no more than two years. Probably the agony of the tumor swelling within her would kill much sooner than that.

"Try and sleep," he said. "I'm going to look to my horse."

Outside the last pale light of day haunted the clearing and the encircling forest. The air stung his nostrils as he walked to the shed where he could hear his horse stamp. The mare had carried him over several years of forest trails, and now as he unfastened the thong that held the door of the shed, she nickered softly to him. He patted her flank. How would he feel if his mare were suffering as the poor woman was suffering? He'd put a ball in her head—or he would simply cut her tumor out. After all, animals were spayed easily enough. To cut out a tumor from the womb would be little more than that. McDowell slapped his horse's side. A doctor dared to do things like that for a horse, but Jane Crawford would have to die a tortured death.

McDowell went back into the cabin. He was surprised to see that Jane Crawford was sleeping. Sleep had wiped the suffering from her face. In the back country, where ignorant people found it hard to tell a quack from a real doctor, a man's reputation meant everything. Could he dare incise this woman? Her eyes opened. She looked at him with such intensity, such vitality that he stepped back from her gaze. The look in her eyes forged his resolve.

"If you think you are prepared to die, I will take the lump from you. You would have to come to Danville," he said.

"I will go with you," she said.

While the fire drove the shadows into the corners of the cabin, Dr. McDowell explained his plan in a calming voice, which seemed to flicker almost as the flames flickered. Since she was still strong enough to make the trip, he was going to take her to his home in Danville, sixty miles away. His instruments, his operating table, and a trained assistant were there. His nephew Jim had just returned from the East, where he had sent him to study medicine.

Tom Crawford refused to let his wife go. He feared that he would never see her again. Four times Dr. McDowell had to explain what he planned to do. Each time Tom listened with mounting apprehension. But finally he gave in. He saddled his horse and rode off to a neighbor's cabin to ask the wife to accompany Jane to Danville.

In the morning Dr. McDowell rode away through a forest sparkling with ice. Mrs. Crawford and her neighbor followed in a few days. Her enormously distended abdomen bounced and scraped against the pommel of the saddle. The two women rode in silence, but at the lonely cabins where they stopped for a drink of water or to take potluck with a frontier family there was a cyclone of talk. Women shook their heads at the terrible thing the doctor was going to do. They clucked their sympathy for Mrs. Crawford, who was riding to Danville to meet her doom beneath the knife of the tall doctor. Men swore and spat.

At last the women reached Danville with its church spire and its single street of frame houses. As they rode down the street past the houses where real window panes glistened, even the doctor's neighbors stared with angry curiosity. At the McDowell house, the doctor met them at the door. His wife helped the suffering frontier mother to a cheerful room and put her to bed. The patient looked about her at the unaccustomed comfort and mercifully slept. That evening the doctor's friends and relatives and finally the minister came to plead and argue that he return the woman uncut to her cabin in Motley's Glen.

"If she must die," said the minister in the courteous tone he kept for another man he believed as well-educated as himself, "it is God's will. But, Ephraim, you are doing the devil's work if you open her with a knife."

None of his callers changed the doctor's resolve. Even his doctor nephew could not shake his purpose. James McDowell strode angrily out of the house. During the days that followed, Ephraim McDowell tended to his patient's diet with care. Throughout his medical practice he made every effort to build up a patient's strength before he operated. At night when she slept, Dr. McDowell studied the illustrations of the abdomen in his medical texts and rehearsed what he would do when it was time for the operation. Each movement of his knife was repeated over and over in his mind before he was satisfied that he was ready. "I'm only waiting for God to smile," he told his patient.

While Dr. McDowell waited for the time when God would smile, God's servant in the church thundered sermons against the butcher who lived among his flock. As the year came round to Christmas, the villagers talked of nothing but the doctor. James McDowell came to see his uncle and urged again that he send Mrs. Crawford home.

"I'm going to operate in the morning."

"You can't. Tomorrow is Christmas!"

"God's beneficence will be at its highest."

That night a tight-lipped Dr. McDowell studied his texts again. Was his effort of the last fifteen years to be wiped out by the pitiful mother's blood? He had returned from Scotland in 1795, and in a few years his fame as a healer had leaped from clearing to clearing until he was renowned throughout the West. In 1802 he had married Sara, the daughter of Governor Isaac Shelby. Practicing in a day before there were stagecoaches, he rode horseback as far as a hundred miles to the bedside of his patients. To cross a flooded stream, he threw the bridle over his horse's head and plunged into the water. He stood erect in his stirrups to escape the driftwood swirling downstream. Once a log collided with his horse and knocked him from the saddle. He managed to swim ashore and hurried, wet and shivering, to his patient. There was scarcely a cabin too remote for him to reach in the great forest he had known since boyhood. Yet if he failed in his operation on Jane Crawford in the morning, he knew the people he had served faithfully would turn against him.

On Christmas morning the sun shimmered on new snow. People filed to church over hard-packed paths that crisscrossed the town. To Dr. James McDowell, hurrying down the street to his uncle's house, the Christmas bells sounded sullen. He had spent a sleepless night. If he could not argue his uncle out of the surgery, he felt bound to help him.

He found Ephraim in the bleak room where, over the years, he had removed many arms and legs mutilated in rough frontier life. There he had taken out kidney stones, a precise work that had helped to make his reputation. In the center of the room stood a plain wooden table. Ephraim acknowledged his nephew's presence as if he had expected it all along. Together they went into Jane Crawford's room.

While the Christmas bells pealed, Ephraim McDowell prayed, "Direct me, oh God, in performing this operation, for I am but an instrument of Thy hands, and am but Thy servant. And if it is Thy will, oh spare this poor, afflicted woman."

Ether had not yet been discovered, and the doctor could only give Mrs. Crawford a few opium pills. He led her down the hallway where the deal planking squeaked under foot. In the doorway to the operating room, she pulled back. Ephraim McDowell gently pulled her along. He strapped her on the table and covered her face with a cloth so she could not see the knives cut.

The two surgeons wore their everyday clothing, but they rolled up their sleeves so as to keep them clean of blood. The surgeon's instruments were spread out on a clean linen cloth. Mrs. McDowell had washed them in strong, homemade soap and water as if they were her best table service. Antiseptics were still unknown, and even the cleanliness that Dr. McDowell always observed was considered by most contemporary doctors to be an eccentricity.

When he had bared the woman's swollen abdomen, Ephraim McDowell took his pen and deftly drew the line for the incision just as he had done in the mind's eye over and over again. He handed the knife to his nephew. To him would go the honor of making the first cut. What they were about to do would either show the way to save countless lives or it would end in the woman's death and possibly their own destruction.

In the church the minister had set aside any thought of Christmas and of God's beneficence to cry out against the devil in his village. An ungodly man was butchering a woman. In frontier language he told his congregation that the evil must be stopped. His frenzied words made his listeners clench their fists.

In the plain room at the house of the surgeon Jane Crawford dug her nails into the rough table boards. She began to sing a familiar hymn. Her voice quavered out loud and strong. James McDowell made the first cut. Then he handed the knife to his uncle who cut deeper into the distorted body. No sooner was the incision made than the intestines, under the terrible pressure from the tumor, tumbled out onto the table.

Still Mrs. Crawford sang. Sweat broke out on McDowell's brow. His cheeks fired red. But his hand continued to cut through to the gelatinous mass of the tumor. At last he could lift the quivering stuff away. The woman sang hymn after hymn. Her voice shook with agony, but she sang. As the doctor cut death away from her vitals, he spoke to her gently and lovingly as if he were comforting a small child. Later he wrote that he, "cut through the Fallopian tube and extracted the sac. We took out 15 pounds of dirty, gelatinous-looking substance."

The minister finished his preaching. The people left the church. They ran to McDowell's house where they could hear the terrible voice singing. Men tore rocks from the frozen ground with their fingers and threw them at the house. They shouted and cried oaths at the surgeon. Awful and tortured above the menace of their voices rose the hymns that they all knew so well. Men battered at the doctor's door until the sheriff and a few others forced them back. A burly frontiersman noosed a rope, and the crowd shouted approval when he looped it over the limb of a tree. Once again the crowd eddied toward the house. The singing grew weaker. It stopped.

Ephraim McDowell gently rolled his patient on her left side to permit the blood to run out. He stitched and plastered the wound. The doctors carried Mrs. Crawford down the hall to her bed. Then Ephraim went to his front door. He stood for a moment looking at the crowd of embittered neighbors, friends who had long honored the old judge and his doctor son. As he studied their faces, men avoided his dark eyes. They dropped stones and shuffled their feet.

"It is over now," he finally said. "If God is kind, everything will be all right."

Somebody in the crowd cheered. Then all at once everybody was cheering and shouting. Women wept.

In five days Jane Crawford was out of bed, fussing with her covers, neatly tucking the spread around her pillow. Dr. McDowell was shocked, but characteristically, the man who first dared to operate on the body cavity began to wonder in 1809 whether it might be better to encourage post-operative patients to leave their beds as soon as possible instead of keeping them still for weeks.

A few weeks after the New Year, Jane Crawford climbed back on the horse that had brought her to Danville. She rode home to the husband who had never expected to see her again and to her children in the cabin in Motley's Glen. She moved west with the westering frontier and lived to be seventy-eight years old. One of the frightened children that Dr. McDowell had comforted in the stricken cabin grew up to become mayor of Louisville.

A fictional story would end here, but the life of a man has a way of continuing on beyond its climax. It was seven years before news of Dr. McDowell's amazing operation reached world medical centers. He waited until he had successfully performed two more ovariectomies before he wrote a brief, three-page article, "Three cases of Extirpation of Diseased Ovaria," which appeared in October 1816, in the *Eclectic Reportory and Analytical Review*, published in Philadelphia. Some surgeons scoffed at the presumptuous idea that a doctor on the frontier could perform such an incredible operation. Most doctors pronounced such surgery far too dangerous. A few doctors in Scotland tried to claim credit for the medical advance. But in Great Britain, France, Germany, Russia, and even in far away India and Ceylon surgeons, taking heart from the frontier surgeon's example, began to save the lives of women stricken with ovarian tumors.

Dr. McDowell himself performed other ovariectomies. One day in 1822 he rode hundreds of miles on horseback to Tennessee where the obese wife of John Overton, the wealthy friend of Andrew Jackson, was dying of a tumor in the womb. With Old Hickory handing him the instruments, he cut through four inches of fat to perform a successful operation. During the course of Ephraim McDowell's life, another doctor nephew, William A. McDowell, estimates he successfully took death from the womb thirteen times. With the discovery of antisepsis, doctors throughout the world were able to perform ovariectomies with relative impunity.

The crowd outside Dr. McDowell's house on that Christmas morning, 1809, had cheered the doctor when they knew Mrs. Crawford would live. But soon ignorant people whispered against him. When he cantered down country roads on his calls, backwoodsmen ran into their houses to escape his "evil eye." Folks said he galloped through the night with the devil by his side. Of course, if you were dying, he could save you.

Ephraim McDowell operated thirty-two times for bladder stones without a death—an amazing record in those times. One of his patients was a gangling seventeen-year-old boy who recovered his health after the doctor removed a large stone. James K. Polk carried the stone in his pocket for good luck and grew up to become President of the United States.

Although they smiled at the frontiersmen's fear of the tall doctor from Danville, other doctors often disparaged him. After his death one of them summed up their attitude: "McDowell was a bold surgeon. He was but a poor fever doctor."

Later doctors said that his contemporaries did not understand him because he was generations ahead of his day. While others bled a fever patient or dosed him with calomel and jalap, Dr. McDowell insisted that nature's healing hand was better. Most doctors prescribed warm water, but he allowed a fevered person to drink cold water. Once he placed a boy naked on the floor and poured buckets of cold water over him to lower his dangerously high temperature.

Doctors might scoff at his merits as a physician, but when it came to surgery, they invariably sent him their most difficult cases. Even though a patient's condition seemed hopeless, McDowell tried to save his life.

"Appearances in surgery are often deceitful," he wrote. "While the taper of life continues to burn, although it be faint, there is yet hope."

In his last years he lived quietly on his farm reading Bobby Burns's poems, singing the comic Scotch songs he had brought home with him from his student days, playing with his grandchildren, and exploring the countryside as he had done as a boy. One day he found a number of small pale blue eggs by a stream on his farm and brought them home. Thinking they were bird's eggs, he put them in a saucer in a warm closet. Later that day a small grandson disobeyed him, and McDowell put the boy into the closet as well. Soon the child pleaded in terror, "Let me out, Grandpa, there is something crawling all over me."

When the boy promised to be good, the doctor opened the door to find the closet swarming with young snakes.

On June 20, 1830, Ephraim McDowell tramped the fields and gorged on strawberries from his patch. He was seized with a terrible pain in the stomach and asked his wife to send for a doctor. He himself thought he had eaten a poisonous insect or eggs on the berries. His doctor said he was suffering from inflammation of the stomach. That night he died. Doctors today believe that Ephraim McDowell, whose brilliant surgery opened the way to the successful removal of a diseased appendix probably died of appendicitis.

Chapter IV

STRANGE PARTNERS

Through the long winter of the northern forests a voyageur worked up a thirst. Cold, he thirsted for whiskey's hot sting. Alone, he thirsted for the trading post, for rough banter, songs, and the sight of man. The American Fur Company post at Mackinac Island was a place to slake a winter's thirst, and on June 6, 1822, hundreds of trappers camped with their furs along the beach below the hilltop fort and milled around the stone building which served the company as a headquarters store.

They celebrated the crisp night and the sunlit day with the contents of many a keg, told their tales of the winter's luck, bawled their songs, and wrestled and danced. Within the store Gurdon Hubbard, a young clerk, watched Alexis St. Martin, an equally young voyageur in the service of the company, shoving his way through the tangle, receiving a clap on the shoulder from this old friend, a rough handshake from another, laughing and joking, moving unwittingly toward a strange fate which would make him famous.

Suddenly a gun's roar stunned the room. A man dropped to his knees in a cloud of acrid smoke and beat out the flames that seared the clothing of a prostrate figure before him.

"I didn't mean to!" he cried. "I didn't mean to kill Alexis!"

Major John Kinzie, who was in charge of the store, took one look at the gaping wound in Alexis' stomach and shouted to a soldier near the door, "Get Surgeon Beaumont!"

As the soldier sprang up the path to the fort, the voyageurs lifted their wounded comrade onto a cot, removed some of his clothing, and tried to stop the gushing blood. These were men who had seen violent death often, and they knew that no man could expect to live with such a terrible hole in his vitals. They had no way of knowing that the obscure surgeon at the nearby army outpost was actually one of the greatest of all surgeons and medical scientists.

Within three minutes by Hubbard's count and twenty minutes by his own, Dr. William Beaumont, resplendent in his braided blue uniform, pushed his way to the bloody bedside and saw at a glance that the youth was "altogether an appalling and a hopeless case." Afterward he set down the details of what he saw. A full blast of duck shot and powder from a gun fired accidentally at only an arm's length had struck Alexis just below his left breast.

"The whole mass of materials forced from the musket, together with fragments of clothing and pieces of fractured ribs, were driven into the muscles and cavity of the chest." Dr. Beaumont was shocked to see, "a portion of the lung, as large as a turkey's egg, protruding through the external wound, lacerated and burnt; and immediately below this, another protrusion, nearly as large as the first, which on further examination proved to be a portion of the stomach, lacerated through all its coats, and pouring out the food he had taken for his breakfast, through an orifice large enough to admit the forefinger."

The protruding lung was caught by its membranes on a sharp point of the fractured rib so that Beaumont could not return it to its proper cavity until he lifted the organ with his finger and clipped off the point of rib with his pen knife. He applied pressure to keep the lung in its place when the patient coughed. Although he considered the youth's condition hopeless, he systematically went about cleansing the wound and applying a dressing. Twenty minutes later Alexis was still miraculously alive, and the doctor commenced removing shot, wadding, and splintered bone. He redressed the wound. As he left his patient, who was too near death to be moved, Gurdon Hubbard heard him say, "The man can't live 36 hours; I will come to see him by and by."

According to Hubbard, Dr. Beaumont returned to see Alexis in two or three hours, "expressing surprise at finding him better than he had anticipated." Beaumont was so encouraged that the next day he brought his instruments and painstakingly removed more shot and shreds of clothing. He snipped off the ragged edges of the wound. The sturdy young voyageur had survived the first obliterating shock, and attended by this remarkable surgeon he now had a slight chance of life.

At this wilderness post on a small island close to the northern shore of Lake Huron, chance had brought together a grievously wounded youth and a doctor whose intelligence was almost uncomfortably acute and whose independence bordered on intransigence. Beaumont was born in Connecticut of Huguenot ancestry in 1785. His home town of Lebanon remembers him to this day as the fourteen-year-old boy who took another lad's dare to stand next to the cannon fired on the village green to celebrate the Fourth of July. The blast injured his eardrum. His ears rang the rest of his life, but he won his dare and the other boy's hunting knife. William Beaumont already had a surgeon's appreciation for fine steel knives, and he triumphantly took his prize home.

He was a surgeon who never saw a sheepskin except on a sheep. Schoolmaster and then storekeeper in backwoods Vermont and New York, he apprenticed himself to Dr. Benjamin Chandler of St. Albans, Vermont, to obtain his medical education. He pounded out powders with mortar and pestle, rolled calomel and quinine pills, swept and dusted the office, and delighted to polish his master's surgical instruments. Mounted on his horse, Traveler, he rode with Dr. Chandler on his rounds. When the doctor amputated a man's arm, his apprentice requested the grisly trophy and spent the entire night carefully dissecting the nerves, blood vessels, and lymph vessels and studying the muscles and bones by candlelight.

On September 7, 1812, Dr. Chandler certified William Beaumont to practice. The new doctor soon joined the Army for the duration of the War of 1812. He proved his surgical brilliance, operating boldly under enemy fire, and proved his compassion, taking the gentlest care of enemy and friend alike. One incident in the war proved unforgettable. He was the surgeon with the U.S. forces that seized York, Ontario. The retreating British blew up the powder magazine, and the onrushing Americans were almost annihilated in the explosion. Surgeon Beaumont, wading in blood, cut off mutilated arms and legs and trepanned heads in a furious effort to save his fellow creatures from untimely deaths.

"I cut and slashed for 48 hours without food or sleep," he remembered all his life. "My God! Who can think of the shocking scene when his fellow creatures lie mashed and mangled in every part with a leg, an arm, a head or a body ground in pieces."

From this nightmare came the remarkable surgical skill which now on the northwest frontier was engaged in saving the life of a young voyageur.

As soon as Alexis could be moved, voyageurs carried him to the one-room frame fort hospital where Beaumont continued emergency treatment. "Under this treatment," he noted, "a strong reaction took place in about 24 hours, accompanied with high arterial excitement, fever and marked symptoms of inflammation of the lining membranes of the chest and abdomen, great difficulty of breathing and a distressing cough."

Alexis, conscious and suffering, endured his night-and-day agony without a word. Five days after the accident muscles and skin in and around the wound sloughed away so that Beaumont could look into the stomach. For ten days Alexis was racked by fever, but his doctor was pleased to see that the wound was taking on a healthy appearance. Everything fed to Alexis ran right out through the wound until Beaumont was able to apply a dressing that kept food within the stomach.

"No sickness," wrote the astounded Beaumont, "nor unusual irritation of the stomach, not even the slightest nausea was manifest during the whole time and after the fourth week the appetite became good, digestion regular."

The vitality of this young outdoorsman proved so great that Beaumont was at last able to report "all the functions of the system perfect and healthy." In the fifth week the case took the dramatic turn which was to give it immortality in medical literature. Beaumont observed that as the external wound contracted and scar tissue began to form, the stomach became firmly attached to the chest wall, but, as the surgeon recorded, "showed not the least disposition to close its orifice."

Plastic surgery was an unknown art in that day, and he saw no way to close the hole. Whenever he dressed the wound, the stomach's contents ran out. Otherwise Alexis continued his incredible recovery. His body expelled bits of shot and splintered bone. At the same time pieces of the shattered ribs flaked off, and the connective tissue at their ends separated. The doctor had to open abscesses and remove fragments of bone and cartilage. Summer faded to fall as the youth and his doctor continued the uphill struggle. When the voyageurs left for the forest, they never expected to see Alexis alive upon their return in the spring. But by April of 1823 he was so well recovered that he could do light chores for his benefactor.

At this time fate, bent on forcing the brilliant doctor and the young voyageur still closer together, acted again. County authorities, their funds exhausted, could no longer pay even a pauper's pittance for the support of the impoverished youth. Instead they offered to send him in an open boat two thousand miles to his home near Montreal. Beaumont knew this would bring death to his convalescing patient.

"Were I reduced to the necessity of existing on the charity of this borough," he wrote in his journal, "I would commit suicide without scruple or hesitation."

There was nothing to do but take the youth into his own family. Only two days after Alexis had been wounded, Deborah Beaumont had given birth to a baby girl. Now into the domestic routine of a young mother taking care of her baby intruded this oddly injured youth, who required exacting care. Sewing, cooking, churning butter, keeping the small Beaumont quarters clean were work enough for this frontier surgeon's wife, but she gladly gave a home to her husband's patient.

"He remained with me, gradually improving, for a year or two," wrote the doctor, "when he became able to walk about and help himself a little, but unable to provide for his own necessities. During this time I nursed him, fed him, clothed him, lodged him and furnished him with every comfort and dressed his wounds daily and for the most part twice a day."

Alexis was now so well recovered that he could chop wood for the family. Although the hole in his stomach remained, nature produced a valve resembling the tongue of a shoe to keep the food inside.

"When he lies on the opposite side, I can look directly into the cavity of the stomach," reported Beaumont, "and almost see the process of digestion."

Digestion was then a mystery to science. William Hunter, a leading anatomist of the time, summed up knowledge on the subject when he told an audience, "Some physiologists will have it that the stomach is a mill, others that it is a fermenting vat, others again that it is a stew pan, but in my view of the matter, it is neither a mill, a fermenting vat, nor a stew pan, but a stomach, gentlemen, a stomach!" Beaumont, an unknown doctor on the western frontier, found himself confronted by a unique opportunity. Through the strange window in the stomach of Alexis St. Martin he could conceivably solve the mystery of how digestion took place. He began to suspend samples of food on a silk string and drop them through the orifice. He let digestion proceed and at carefully timed intervals pulled the food out again for observation.

"I can pour in water with a funnel," he wrote down in his case book, "or put in food with a spoon, and draw them out again with a syphon. I have frequently suspended flesh, raw and wasted, and other substances into the perforation to ascertain the length of time required to digest each; and at one time used a tent of raw beef, instead of lint, to stop the orifice, and found that in less that five hours it was completely digested off, as smooth and even as if it had been cut with a knife."

All the foods found in a frontier post were used in the experiments. Alexis' stomach showed Beaumont and science what it could do to grains such as rice and barley; apples, oranges; meats including lamb, turkey, salted pork, and roast beef; carrots, turnips, and potatoes; and bread, cake, and dumplings. Sometimes Beaumont withdrew gastric juice from the stomach and, keeping it at body heat in vials, placed pieces of food in it. At last he was ready to publish his first paper in the *Medical Recorder*.

He presented his facts clearly and simply and then added, "These demonstrate, at least, that the stomach secretes a fluid which possesses solvent properties. The change in the solid substances is effected too rapidly to be accounted for on the principle of either maceration or putrefaction." The scientific world, recognizing the care that had gone into Beaumont's work, accepted these first research findings from the frontier partnership of a military surgeon and a voyageur.

The partnership from which important scientific findings were yet to come was an uneasy one from the start. Longing for his old life in the forest, intemperate, given to drunken binges, and loathing the experiments carried on in his stomach, Alexis soon forgot the debt he owed the man who had saved his life. He could not understand the precise doctor and his quest. Beaumont grew increasingly exasperated at the moody behavior of his unwilling colleague. Alexis sulked, and the doctor stormed.

In 1825 Beaumont went on leave to his wife's home at Plattsburg, New York, and brought the rebellious Alexis with him. At first the experiments with gastric juice went well, but then one day Alexis vanished. Plattsburg was temptingly close to the Canadian border, and the youth had fled to his Quebec home. There, while Beaumont searched anxiously for him, he married Marie Jolly and went off into the Indian country as a voyageur for the Hudson's Bay Company. It was not until July 1827 that Beaumont, by then stationed at Fort Howard, on Lake Michigan's Green Bay, heard of Alexis. W. W. Matthews, who toured Canada every winter hiring voyageurs for the American Fur Company, wrote to him:

"While in Canada last winter, I succeeded in finding your ungrateful boy, Alexis St. Martin. He is married and lives about 12 miles back from Berthier at a place called LaChalaupe. He is poor and miserable beyond description, and his wound is worse than when he left you."

Several fur-company men joined Matthews in persuading Alexis to go back to Beaumont, who was now stationed on the Upper Mississippi River, and resume the experiments which had been broken off at a highly critical point. Beaumont at last was able to note down:

"They succeeded in engaging him and transported him from lower Canada, with his wife and two children to me at Fort Crawford, Prairie du Chien, Upper Mississippi, a distance of nearly 2,000 miles in August, 1829. His stomach and side were in a similar condition as when he left me in 1825. The aperature was open, and his health good."

With a wife and children to support Alexis now drove a hard bargain. He would submit to a new series of experiments, but his family should be given board and lodging and he should receive 800 livres, about $300 a year. Beaumont had to meet this new expense out of his skimpy army surgeon's pay.

Beaumont had already proved that gastric juice was a solvent and digestion was not just a process of maceration brought about by body heat. Now he established with the aid of chemists that the principle ingredient of gastric juice was hydrochloric acid. He showed that gastric juice appears only when food enters the stomach or is chewed. He investigated the phenomenon of taste and indicated that the sense of taste stimulated the flow of digestive juices. He endeavored to find out exactly what hunger and thirst were. His laboratory equipment consisted only of a thermometer, test tubes, and a sand bath, but while he had access to Alexis' stomach he continued to make new discoveries. When Alexis became gloomy, Beaumont studied the effects of his emotions on digestion. Alexis was a man who counted his days as long dry stretches between drinks. When his partner suffered a hangover from too much whiskey, Beaumont checked his stomach's condition.

His careful records established that the human stomach takes from three to three and a half hours to dissolve and mix food before it is passed into the intestines. Meats and cereals are easier to digest than are vegetables. Placing a thermometer in Alexis' stomach, he discovered the temperature to be 100 degrees Fahrenheit, certainly not enough to cook food as a means of digestion, as some thought, but undoubtedly an aid to the process. He proved that gastric juices, far from causing fermentation, prevented it.

Parents who tell their children to chew their food well are profiting from one of his discoveries. He learned that digestion was "facilitated by minuteness of division and tenderness of fibre, and retarded by opposite qualities."

Even Dr. Beaumont had to agree to a vacation for his colleague with the window in his stomach, and in 1831 Alexis loaded his wife and children into a canoe and paddled down the Mississippi to the Ohio River, and up the Ohio to Marietta. They crossed Ohio to Lake Erie from which they went to Lake Ontario and down the St. Lawrence to home. A man who could make such a trip was far from being an invalid.

To Dr. Beaumont's surprised pleasure, Alexis returned on time and signed his "X" to a contract for another year's experiments. Beaumont, who in Alexis' absence had gone through the Black Hawk War with the troops and fought an epidemic of Asiatic cholera, now renewed the research. By 1833 he was able to publish his *Experiments and Observations on the Gastric Juice and the Physiology of Digestion*. He began a fourth group of sixty-two tests, which established conclusively his findings.

He planned other tests, but Alexis tired once and for all of eating for science, of having his food removed from his stomach and thermometers inserted into his body. He paddled his canoe into the north country and refused to return. On June 26, 1834, he had a friend write a letter to the doctor, which ended with a curt, "No more from yours, Alexis St. Martin." The strange partnership was at an end, but it had produced 238 published experiments which made medical history.

Medical scientists have praised Beaumont's devotion to truth and remarkable gifts as an observer. They pointed out that his

1. Unkempt and bewhiskered, a frontier doctor rode sixty miles to make a call and slept out of doors on the ground.
Culver Picture Service

2. Ephraim McDowell, M.D., father of abdominal surgery
Courtesy of the American Medical Association

3. Surgeon William Beaumont
Courtesy of the American Medical Association

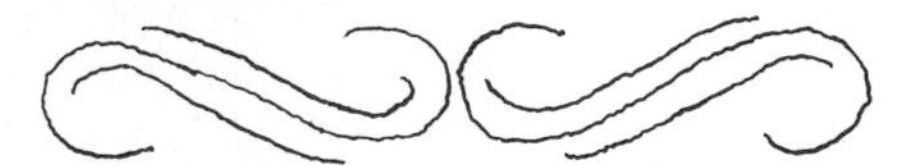

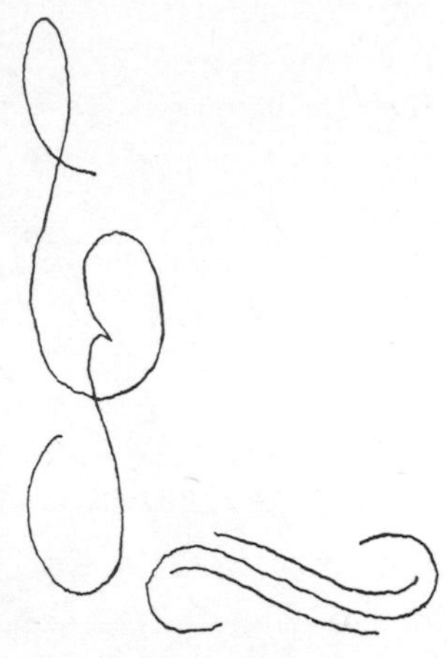

4. Dr. Daniel Drake explored the interior of the continent to study diseases. *Courtesy Denver Medical Society*

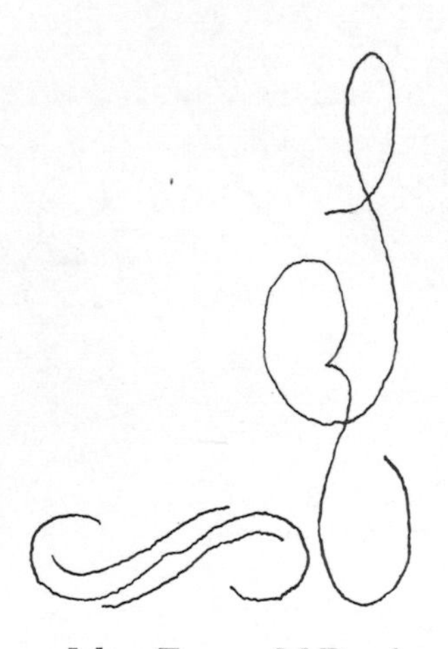

5. John Evans, M.D., frontier doctor, railroad builder, and second governor of Colorado. *Denver Public Library Western Collection*

experiments preceded those of Pavloff with dogs by half a century. Sir William Osler felt justified in calling him "the first great American physiologist." His last years were spent in St. Louis, then the gateway to the Far West. In 1849 at the age of sixty-four Beaumont fought a deadly cholera epidemic with the same resolution which had saved Alexis' life. While carrying on a medical practice, he tried to persuade Alexis to resume their partnership. But Alexis would not return.

On a frigid night in 1853 the man who was known on the frontier as the good doctor who worked miracles slipped on the ice as he returned home from treating a patient and struck his head on his porch steps. On April 25, 1853, he died of his injuries. Alexis St. Martin outlived his partner in medical research by twenty-seven years. When he died at the age of eighty-six, his family denied his internationally famous stomach to medical science. They buried Alexis secretly in an unmarked grave dug eight feet beneath his native soil.

Chapter V

A MEDICAL BAEDEKER

When the boy was restless and talkative in his bed at night, his mother said, "Be still and go to sleep, or the Shawnees will catch you."

In 1844 the man the boy became remembered this as he camped with the Shawnees, now in exile where the Kansas River flows into the Missouri. He smiled as he heard Indian mothers frighten their naughty children with the threat of capture by tribes still more savage.

The boy milked the cows for his mother, but both mother and son were mortified when a stranger came by and saw him. A boy on the Kentucky frontier could churn butter without being taunted for doing women's work, but he could not milk a cow.

In 1842 the man remembered this as, riding a trail through pines and birches on the shores of Lake Superior, he met an Indian family coming toward him. The father, defying the custom of his tribe that only a woman should carry a pack, bore his wife's heavy load on his shoulders. When they caught sight of him, the Indians fled into the woods, where the woman took the pack on herself.

In 1791, when he was six years old, the boy went to his Aunt Lydia's wedding. Men brought their firearms and galloped away in pursuit of Indians as soon as the vows were exchanged. One day a settler, warming himself at a campfire, was killed by Indians. Neighbors carried the hideous remains through the village on a litter. Evenings before the fireplace in the cabin the boy's father and his friends talked of the Indian wars, of midnight butcheries, of captivities, of torture. The sleeping boy often dreamed of Indians stalking him through nightmare forests. He kept an ax and scythe under his bed for defense. The man, remembering this, wrote a letter about his boyhood to his own children and said, "In the morning, the first duty was to ascend to the loft and look through the cracks for Indians, lest they might have planted themselves near the door to rush in when the strong cross-bar should be removed and the heavy latch raised."

The boy carried the fear of Indians, of torture and death in his heart, but the man traveled alone into the Far West among Indians, trappers, and mountain men. The boy, sent into the woods to look for the cows, broke bushes to guide himself back to the clearing. The man found his way unaided from the Alleghenies to the Rockies, from the Gulf of Mexico to the Canadian north woods when all the region was a wilderness.

Riding to the water mill with a heavy bag of corn across his saddle, the nine-year-old boy noticed the influence of the soils on the character of the forest. Sometimes he went to barter for salt above the Blue Licks and he saw that along the trail the rocky terrain and evergreens went together. The man roamed the interior of the continent observing topography, meteorology, plants, animals, rocks, water, and people to understand the diseases endemic in the land. He pursued diseases as his friend Audubon pursued birds.

The engaging boy, sprightly, blue-eyed, and curly-haired, became the austere man Dr. Daniel Drake, whom his patient Harriet Beecher Stowe, described as having "a tall, rectangular, perpendicular sort of body, as stiff as a poker," a man with penetrating eyes that crinkled with emotion, a man who ran with tireless steps to keep his appointments and wore a gold chain around his neck with a watch attached.

Daniel Drake was born on October 20, 1785, at Plainfield, New Jersey, the son of Isaac Drake, who tended the gristmill on the Bound Brook branch of the Raritan River. It was a family tradition that the Drakes were descended from Sir Francis Drake. If this were true they had descended far since the days of the Elizabethan sea rovers; Daniel's father was hard pressed to make a living for his wife and children. When the boy was three years old, Isaac decided to take his family beyond the mountains to Kentucky, where there was room for an impoverished man to start over again.

Daniel crawled into the two-horse Jersey wagon beside his parents, and they jounced over the weary mountain roads to Fort Pitt, where they went aboard a flatboat for the dangerous trip down the Indian-haunted Ohio to the western country. The family came ashore near what is now Maysville, Kentucky. One night they were encamped on a high hill beyond Johnson's Fork of the Licking River, when a chorus of wolf howls echoed in the forest. Indians often signaled their attack with wolf calls, and the family fled from their wagons, horses, and telltale fire into the dark, where they crouched terrified in the bushes. When they saw real wolves sifting among the trees like shadows, they hugged one another with relief and hurried back to the fire, which now meant safety. The Drakes had arrived in a forest so savage that even a pack of wolves on the prowl was more welcome than its human inhabitants.

Near the rude Kentucky outpost of Washington, Father Drake, reduced to one dollar in cash, began to clear his thirty-eight-acre claim. He built a dwelling, which Daniel later described as his earliest memory, "a log cabin, one story high without a window, with a door opening to the south, with a half-finished wooden chimney, with a roof on one side only, without any upper or lower floor." Later the Drakes added a puncheon floor below and a clapboard floor above, a small square window and a chimney. On the last day of August 1789, a frost killed their ripening corn, and the family would have starved except for the plentiful game. Wild turkeys were so fat that when shot from the trees, their skins burst against the ground. Still, there was no bread, and Daniel never forgot his bread hunger and how he begged his parents.

"I would often cry and beg for bread when we were seated around the table till they would have to leave it and cry themselves," he wrote in manhood.

In the years that followed Daniel grubbed stumps with mattock and ax, hacked down saplings, lopped limbs from trees felled by his father, and burned the brush in piles as the Drakes enlarged their fields of wheat. The family was poor, but now they had bread. The winter that he was five, Daniel fell on the ice. Dr. William Goforth rode out from town to heal the abscess that formed on his spine. As he worked on the boy's back, the child asked such pertinent medical questions that the doctor smilingly called him, "Dr. Drake." Whenever an itinerant school teacher happened by, Daniel went to school in a log schoolhouse by the crick where hickory switches grew in handy proximity. His illiterate father and mother shared his joy when, at seven years of age, he learned to read. When he was nine he dropped out of school for two years to help clear more forest and build a new cabin. He reveled in the bird songs, the wild flowers, and the ancient elms. He asked himself questions about the soil, the weather, the things that grew or ran in the forest.

Daniel's cousin John, the son of a prosperous Kentucky frontier storekeeper, was sent east to the University of Pennsylvania to study medicine. He promised that when he graduated, he would teach Daniel the rudiments. Meanwhile he loaned his used medical books to the boy, who read them with the same avidity that he devoured each word—advertisements and all—of the rare newspapers that reached the backwoods farm.

Daniel sat bareback on the lean horse and guided it as it pulled the plow. Working in the harvest field, he noticed that men sweated more than boys. His ambition was to sweat enough to wet his shirt. He scalded his left knee making soap, wove baskets from saplings, turned over rocks in the streams to look for crawfish, puzzled over the approach of thunderstorms and set out pans to catch the rainwater. He marked that only opossums and ants ate pawpaws.

How does a parent recognize the bright symptoms of genius in a child? This is a matter that troubles the competitive parents of today, but Daniel's father and mother, weary with labor, distracted by fear of Indians, had no time to ponder how extraordinary their son was. When his cousin John died soon after graduation, it seemed that Daniel was destined to a frontier farmer's life. Then, when he was fifteen years old, Dr. Goforth asked the backwoods boy to come to Cincinnati, population 400, where he would make a physician and a gentleman out of him. Daniel's father was to pay a fee of $400.

In December 1800, after a tearful good-by to home, Daniel rode to Cincinnati, where he read books in the doctor's library, compounded salves, mixed drugs, and rode with his master on his rounds. That year Daniel made his first contribution to science. He became a guinea pig. Smallpox vaccine had reached America from England, and Dr. Goforth was one of the first New World doctors to try it out. He inoculated Daniel. The youth remained healthy and continued to clear his way through the Latin phrases of the doctor's books. Years later Daniel Drake wrote his children about the doctor's home in which he lived and studied.

"Few of you have seen the genuine old doctor's shop. Or regaled your olfactory nerves in the mingled odors, which like incense to the god of physic, arose from brown paper bundles, bottles stopped with worm-eaten corks, and open jars of ointment not a whit behind those of the apothecary in the days of Solomon. Yet such a place is very well for the student. However idle, he will always be absorbing a little medicine; especially if he sleep beneath the greasy counter."

Daniel absorbed enough medicine by the time he was nineteen that Dr. Goforth awarded him the first medical diploma ever given west of the Alleghenies and took him into his practice. The young doctor rode horseback to the cabins of his patients. He carried few instruments in his saddlebags but plenty of Glauber's salts, Dover's powders, paregoric, vermifuges, blisters, Peruvian bark for fevers, dragon's blood, gamboge, and nux vomica. His fees were calculated at twenty-five cents a mile, with half the amount deducted if the patient fed his horse. Often he took his fees in corn, venison, or wild honey.

In 1805 Daniel Drake, aided once more by his father, traveled east to Philadelphia. He was too poor to buy a ticket to the hospital library, but he worked for five months in the clinics. He attended the lectures of the great Dr. Benjamin Rush and returned to the West inspired by his teacher's eloquence and dedication.

Reaching the frontier, he hung out his shingle at Mayslick and married Harriet Sisson, daughter of Colonel Jared Sisson.

"We began the world in love and hope and poverty," he said.

Dr. Drake battled the prevalent typhus, malaria, and catarrh. He relieved diphtheria or the croup by holding a suffering child upside down by the feet and tickled a congested throat with feathers soaked in goose grease until the patient vomited and cleared the obstruction. Believing in the infectious nature of diseases, he ascribed autumnal fever to "living organic forms, too small to be seen with the naked eye, and which belong either to the vegetable or animal kingdom or partake of the characters of both." He noticed that General Scott's troops spread cholera on the way to the Black Hawk War. At a time when others thought cholera and malaria alike were caused by marsh emanations, he attributed cholera to animicular bodies.

Combative in his opinions, caustic of tongue, Dr. Drake made bitter enemies of many physicians. Hastening through the streets at more of a run than a walk, his hat under his arm, he seemed to Dr. Samuel Gross, "as if inviting the morning breeze to fan his temple and cool his burning brain."

Once as he hurried along he was stopped by a doctor whom he had offended.

"I don't propose to step out of the way of a fool," said the man.

"I will," replied Drake, and stepped aside.

Patients came from all over the West to consult Dr. Drake. Among these was Henry Clay, who became a firm friend. Even the doctor's bitter political, social, and professional enemies sent for him whenever there was a serious illness in their family. They kept out of his way while he was in the house.

On January 1, 1841, Abraham Lincoln was to be married to Mary Todd, daughter of a leading Kentucky family, but he failed to appear. That night he was found wandering through the back streets of Springfield in a dazed condition. There followed two years of illness, during which Lincoln wrote to Dr. Drake for medical advice. No doctor practicing today would be surprised at Drake's response. Lincoln's friend, Joshua Speed said afterwards, "I remember Dr. Drake's reply—which was that he would not undertake to prescribe for him without a personal interview."

Drake, who in his lifetime was to see the American frontier move west over a thousand miles, was a pioneer to the heart. He opened the first drugstore in Cincinnati in 1807 and in 1816 fitted it out with the first soda fountain in the West. He founded a circulating library in Cincinnati in 1811, and in 1820 he established a museum for the study of western antiquities and natural history. When a young man walked into the museum and asked to be made the collector and taxidermist, Drake made him curator. The young man was John James Audubon. Drake wrote about the West too, and in 1810 he published *Notices Concerning Cincinnati*, which contained the first description of the backwoods disease called the "trembles" and surprised Easterners by the precise detail of his observations and the clarity of his writing. Seventy-three years before Gifford Pinchot he urged that the supposedly illimitable forests be preserved. He advocated tree surgery. More important, he established the first hospital on the Ohio River, and he edited the *Western Medical and Physical Journal*. Standard-bearer of a new western culture, Daniel Drake was called the first citizen of Cincinnati, the Benjamin Franklin of the frontier.

Drake wrote poetry too, including a song, "The Buckeye Tree" set to the tune of "Yankee Doodle." It was he who eulogized the buckeye and suggested that Ohio be called, "The Buckeye State." He gave temperance lectures. One hot summer afternoon he was addressing a crowd on the merits of avoiding too much drink when the heat became too intense to be borne without solace. He led the crowd across the street to a saloon where all had a cooling libation. Then Drake, who never confused abstinence with temperance, completed his address.

As a father, Drake was affectionate and emotional but firm to the point of rigor. One of his sons, Charles Daniel Drake, who later became a United States senator from Missouri, attributed his success to the intensive care his father had given to his training and education. He was an intense husband too, who never gave up mourning the loss of his wife. After her death he always wore a piece of black crepe in his hat.

Daniel Drake's life on the frontier had taught him how to meet disaster, and when, on September 18, 1829, his sister-in-law, Caroline Sisson's bed caught on fire as she slept, he rushed into the room and bravely compressed the burning covers with his naked hands until the fire was out. Caroline was badly charred and died eight hours later. The doctor's hands were so seriously burned that it was months before he could use them again. Then with a physician's objectivity he wrote up a report, "History of Two Cases of Burn, Producing Serious Constitutional Irritation."

He believed that medicine on the westering frontier had two big jobs. He thought doctors should investigate the health and sanitation of the wilderness and insure a supply of physicians in the West. To insure the supply of physicians he founded two medical schools and taught in seven different schools. One third of the doctors practicing in the Ohio River Valley in his lifetime had been his students. One of them, Dr. Samuel D. Gross, recalled his teacher in the classroom. Drake, he said, was ever the precise surgeon with his words but at the same time was eloquent and given to sallies of wit. Dr. Gross, no mean wielder of words himself said, "In his lectures he seemed always to be wrestling with his subject, viewing and exhibiting it in every possible aspect and relation and never stopping until like an ingenious and dexterous anatomist, he had divested it by means of his mental scalpel of all extraneous matter."

Drake spent so much of his life in teaching and fending for his principles in the bitter controversies that raged through the medical schools of his day that he could honestly say toward the end of his life, "Medical schools have consumed me."

Investigating the health and sanitation of the wilderness proved far more congenial to the man who as a boy had loved the forest. He first conceived this vast undertaking in 1810, but he was already past fifty years old when he set out in May 1836, to crisscross the six million square miles of wilderness which extended from the Gulf to Hudson Bay, from the Alleghenies to the Rockies. He traveled 30,000 miles to take temperatures, make barometrical observations, check elevations, test water, study vegetation, animals, and minerals. He went in skiffs, on railroads, steamboats, stagecoaches, buggies, common wagons, on horseback, muleback, and on foot. He was determined to learn the influence of climate, water supply, and environment on health. Soil, diet and drink, the occupations and pursuits of Indians, Negroes and whites all had to be investigated. He wanted to know if climate, negligence, indigestion and tobacco could cause the early decay of teeth, if premature marriages were a health problem on the frontier, whether migration into the West lengthened life. He marked out wilderness lead mines and salt works for detailed health studies.

Lonely doctors in remote settlements, medicine men, white Indian practitioners, and old grannies with a knack for curing were astounded to have a tall man in black appear out of the woods and to learn that he was the legendary Dr. Drake, come to talk to them about the health conditions in their vicinity. Intent as he was on charting the diseases endemic in the wilderness, he still never failed to turn aside for a worthwhile purpose. He auscultated the chest of the dying Seminole chief, Tiger Tail, and heard, "the palpitations of his savage but patriotic heart." He cared for the sick wherever he went, wrote poetry, and, among other things, tossed sleeplessly through hot southern nights in feather beds which he loathed and complained about the ignorance of St. Louis in the "art and mystery of scavengering."

Sometimes he wrote about what he saw in his travels. From the lower Mississippi he reported that "whole families and whole schools of girls titilate their nervous systems with snuff. They become so thoroughly impregnated with the powder, that their apparel might hang in a hot room the whole summer without being touched by the moths. We know of but two advantages from the habit. First, it may render them insensible to the breath of the other sex, who begin the use of tobacco with the study of grammar. Second, it can be made a substitute for whiskie."

After a dusty ride across the plains, he attacked the stagecoach as a means of travel for invalids. "The stage coach," he said, "hung on springs, gives but little exercise on smooth roads, while, from the speed with which it is driven, it subjects weakly passengers to excessive jolting over rough ones. In the former case, its celerity and easy swing often produce nausea, which being seldom carried to the point of full vomiting, has most of the distressing attributes of sea sickness, without any of the ulterior benefits."

He found steamboats, "thronged, restless and noisy, and the air of the crowded lodging rooms is necessarily confined." Dr. Drake considered it salubrious to walk and recommended to invalids that they ride horseback. Struggling through the matted rushes at the Mississippi's mouth to check the breeding grounds of insects, camping with Indians on the high plains to learn about herbs and roots, accompanying Canadian boatmen down foaming rapids to see what the effects of frequent dunkings were on their health, venturing onto the stormy waters of Lake Superior to take its temperature, he pressed his astounding inquiry. At Sault Ste. Marie, the doctor, who suffered from dyspepsia, tasted whitefish and acclaimed it the "food of the nymphs. He who tastes it once will thenceforth be unable to relish that of any other fish."

This may account for his scorn for the meals he ate as he journeyed year after year through the wilderness. "In the West," he said, "there are three standing traveler's dishes, which every invalid should refuse, or eat with fear and trembling. These are; chickens who sing their own death-song under his dining-room windows and are transferred from the aviary to the table with less of culinary than vital heat in their systems. 2. Rancid and fat bacon, fried with eggs until their albumen is coagulated into horn. 3. Hot, unleavened biscuit, saturated with lard, kneaded the moment before they are committed to the pan and served up while they still send forth columns of vapor and volatile oil."

While his contemporaries rhapsodized about the romantic exploits and vigor of the flatboatmen, Dr. Drake, who traveled with them often, was objective about their ways. He observed that they were for a long period exposed to the river atmosphere, their diet consisted chiefly of bread and meal, they drank whiskey to excess, and they returned upstream by river only with great toil. He noted that many died of fevers contracted from lying through the night on the river banks and that rheumatism and pulmonary diseases were the lot of the others.

His account of the life of steamboaters is equally revealing. On western steamboats, he said, men and boys lived an exposed and reckless life. Firemen and deckhands ate chiefly bread and meat with coffee in the morning, were exposed to weather, and were often in the water trying to free their boat from a sandbar or snag. Firemen worked in temperatures of from 120 to 150 degrees. The doctor took the pulses of firemen and entered in his journal that their pulses jumped to 130–40 a minute in the heat of the furnace room. The steamboat men drank ardent spirits and suffered from diarrhea, intermittent fever with disordered spleen, and dropsy. Often they were drowned or scalded to death.

Dr. Drake ascended northern rivers to the Rockies with French voyageurs in their canoes and Mackinac boats. He commented on the French, who, reinforced by their own offspring by Indian women, ranged the forests. "In the use of alcoholic drinks, they were of necessity temperate, except when in port. Tobacco they never dispensed with. Their diet consisted essentially of maize or Indian corn; the variety called white flint being preferred. It was boiled in a lye of wood ashes until the outer integument could be rubbed off and then put in sacks. A quart of this corn, with two ounces of tallow, or hard fat, boiled through the night, constituted the ration of a voyageur for the ensuing day."

Although the voyageurs were below ordinary Anglo-American standards in height, Drake found them "muscular and very strong, from being compelled to carry heavy burdens, including their canoes, around the shoals and rapids of the rivers on which they run." He made notes on their diseases. Those on the Missouri River suffered from ague and fever, but those on rivers farther north were bedeviled by rheumatism.

In the far Southwest the indefatigable doctor, intent on compiling his medical Baedeker of the interior of the continent traveled with the Sante Fe traders, accompanying caravans of up to two hundred men. "Their diet," he said, "is generally composed of cakes of flour, bacon and the flesh of the bison, and coffee, to which beans and crackers are sometimes added. They often suffer for want of water." He explained that the men slept beneath their wagons or in tents at first but after passing the 101 or 102 degree of west longitude there was so little dew that no shelter was necessary at night. These men, he could for once report, enjoyed good health.

For ten years he traveled through the wilderness. He spent only winter months at home sorting his notes and studying. Teaching had drained him, but travel, he said, added twelve years onto his life. He advised the elderly to travel. Whenever he could he took his wife or one of his grown children with him on his trips.

In 1850 Drake published his nineteen-hundred-page, *A Systematic, Historical, Etiological and Practical Treatise on the Principal Diseases of the Interior Valley of North America.*

Usually the conservative medical world takes decades to accept a major work of science, but Drake's masterpiece of research was greeted with immediate enthusiasm. This intensely American work of genius, literally drawn from the heart of the continent, started from the premise that natural diseases are influenced by the character of soil, climate, temperature, and food. Six hundred pages described physical elements of the terrain over which Drake had traveled so determinedly. Then separate sections treated each of the major categories of diseases, relating them directly to the people, their way of life, and the land in which they lived.

Alexander von Humboldt called the vast study, "a treasure among scientific works." Medical reviews acclaimed it, "an enduring monument of American genius," and "the greatest work of pure science ever produced in America." The first year of its appearance the American Medical Association met in Cincinnati. Dr. Alfred Stille of Philadelphia, chairman of the committee on medical literature, devoted his entire report to Drake's work. He named it, "an achievement of which every doctor in America should be proud." Drake was present and listened, head bowed, as the doctor delegates from all over the nation applauded with an ardor which Americans usually reserve for national political conventions. Finally he arose. The cheers became more frenzied. He made his way to the podium, where he tried to quiet his colleagues. At last the hall grew silent. Drake tried to talk, but his voice failed. Helped to a chair, he covered his face with his hands and wept. Drake always claimed that he inherited two traits from his tender mother—he shed tears with ease and possessed an irresistible desire to fall asleep in church. Here on the stage, perhaps remembering the striking events that had carried him from a rude boyhood in a Kentucky frontier cabin to the acclaim of his nation's medical profession, he wept. The man who many ranked second only to Abraham Lincoln among the orators of the West could not speak.

The delegates boomed him for president of the A.M.A., but he refused to let his name be placed before the nominating committee. An eastern doctor with more polish and learning could better represent American medicine to the world. He belonged in the West. Drake returned to work on a sequel to his book.

Drake the patriot, always in demand to speak on public occasions, was asked to address a public gathering in Cincinnati, on the night of October 26, 1852, to honor the memory of Daniel Webster, who had just died. Although suffering from a cold, he accepted and made a stirring address. That night he experienced a severe chill, but the next day he lectured as usual at the college at noon. The day after that he was confined to bed by fever and coughing. His daughter sat by his bedside. Daniel Drake tried to feel his own pulse. He raised his hands to observe the nervous twitching.

"You have had that ever since you were sick," she said reassuringly.

"Yes, my sickness in 1825 left me in this condition," he said.

Apparently satisfied with his diagnosis, he shortly turned on his side and fell into a sweet sleep in which there were no dreams of Indians stalking through nightmare forests, no hunger for bread, no medical quarrels, no hardships on the trail, no diseased patients calling upon his skill and devotion.

Chapter VI

SPANISH DOCTORS

The chain of living smallpox virus stretched from arm to arm across the sea from Spain to Texas.

In 1803 the king's physician, Francisco Xavier de Balmis, and two assistants set sail from Spain in a mercy galleon bound for the smallpox-plagued New World. Their cargo was a quantity of dried smallpox virus on threads and 22 children, who were to form a living chain of vaccine carriers. Each week as the ship furrowed the ocean, two children were vaccinated with virus taken from the sores on the arms of the two vaccinated the week before. Dr. de Balmis hovered anxiously over each pair of inoculations because he knew he must bring the virus alive to the New World. Only then could he carry out the king's directive to vaccinate from "arm to arm to all that may come, furnishing it free to the poor." Spaniards who had inadvertently introduced smallpox to the New World were striving to stamp it out.

The ship landed in Mexico with its chain of living virus unbroken, and Dr. Xavier de Balmis set about vaccinating the population. Finally on April 8, 1806, the life-saving virus reached Texas on the remote frontier of the Spanish Empire. The provincial governor of Texas at Bexar, now San Antonio, reported to the commanding general in Mexico City, "I received the vial with the vaccine fluid, and the paper full of scabs of smallpox which accompanied it. The first of this month I placed 12 children—six belonging to the troops and six belonging to the settlers—in a room in the temporary military hospital. They received the operation and remained under the care of the physician until the work of transferring the matter from arm to arm was accomplished."

Adults, confident that the innocent children were free of blood diseases, readily accepted vaccination from them. At a time when Jenner's 1798 publication on smallpox vaccination was still unknown through much of Europe and only six years after Dr. Goforth vaccinated his pupil, Daniel Drake, on the Anglo-American frontier, Spanish medicine was striking a great blow against death by plague on the distant plains of Texas.

In their zeal the Spanish doctors even vaccinated the Indians, who, not having a white man's inherited resistance to the disease, were suffering fearful losses. As recently as 1780 when Indians were dying in great numbers in his vicinity, Domo Cabello had written to the governor from Presidio of Bahia del Espiritu that he did not wish "to be thought uncharitable, but that it would not be greatly regretted if the whole tribe were exterminated, since they were so harmful despite their apparent peace and friendliness."

Most Spaniards shared Cabello's view. Even the more humane among them did little to help the stricken tribes because there was no medicine available. In the sunset days of Spanish power in what is now our Southwest, Spain won a last triumph, which unlike its earlier bloody victories over man was a triumph over one of the most dreaded foes of all mankind.

Spanish doctors in the Southwest were fighting disease when the English settlements still hugged the Atlantic coast. They were trained in Spain or at the University of Mexico, which as early as 1578 had a school of medicine offering such advanced courses as comparative anatomy, and by 1583 was teaching human anatomy with the aid of cadavers.

When in April 1540, Francisco Vasquez de Coronado set out from Culiacán to search for the seven cities of Cibola in the wilderness north of Mexico, he brought a doctor with him. Coronado explored the mountains and what he described as "sandy heaths, smooth and wearisome and bare of wood" for cities of gold but found only the ancestors of the present-day Pueblo Indians, who on more than one occasion fought back against the Spaniards' cruelty. In one battle Coronado was pierced with a poison arrow, but the doctor treated his wounds with quince juice and saved his life.

Not all the Spanish who followed were bent on conquest; sandaled padres sought to save the souls of the heathen Indians, and one doctor at least explored the wilderness for plants and medicines. He was Francesco Hernandez, personal physician to Philip II, who at the king's request spent the years 1570–77 in the New World to discover herbs and roots that would alleviate the suffering of the sick.

In 1769 Galvez, Royal Visitador-General, and Fray Junipero Serra set out in two ships from LaPaz, Mexico, to colonize Alta California. Don Pedro Prat, graduate in medicine from the University of Barcelona and captain in the Royal Spanish Army, was aboard the *San Carlos*, which sailed before the *San Antonio* but arrived much later with a grim tale of disease at sea to tell.

The ship put in at Cedros Island to replenish its water casks from springs which were contaminated. The captain lost his way in the coastal fogs, and the ship wandered for 110 days, while Dr. Prat struggled against a virulent dysentery and scurvy, which killed every member of the crew but one sailor and the cook. When the ship arrived in San Diego Bay, the surviving passengers were so weak they could not lower the boat to go ashore, and the crew of the *San Antonio* had to come aboard to help them.

On the sandy shores Dr. Prat and the *San Antonio*'s men built a refuge of sails, awning, driftwood, and earth to shelter the sick. It was the first hospital in California. The doctor made soup from hardtack, and although convalescing from dysentery, he tramped through hill meadows looking for herbs to cure the aching bones and sore and bleeding gums of his patients. The *San Antonio*'s crew also fell ill.

On October 15 the Indians attacked the hospital without warning. Dr. Prat gathered up his sick and fled to the ships. The Spaniards fought fiercely until the Indians broke off and ran for the cover of the hills. Then the doctor returned ashore and treated the Indian wounded left on the battleground. He once again tended the sick, who died in such numbers that the site of the tent hospital is still called Dead Man's Point. Soon only one Spaniard was left out of every three who had set out to establish a new realm in California. Spanish chronicles say that the doctor's mind snapped in the ordeal. He went to newly founded Monterey as the first surgeon-general, but demented by his experiences, he died in 1771.

As on the Anglo-American frontier, it was the military surgeon who first brought the art of healing to the settlements. Doctors stationed with coastal garrisons received occasional help from the surgeons of visiting ships. At the missions throughout the Southwest, padres also treated the sick but with indifferent results. Few priests had any medical knowledge, although Father Luis Gil y Taboada is shown in California records as having been so "skilled as a physician" that he performed Caesarean sections on Indian women dying in childbirth. Father Marcelino Marquinez at Mission Santa Cruz from 1810 to 1817 was expert enough to amputate an arm.

Garrison surgeons rode out from the presidio to missions and ranches as far as a hundred miles away, where they treated the prevalent scurvy, chronic dysentery, dropsy, syphilis, and tuberculosis. Pablo Saler, Surgeon at Monterey from 1791 to 1800, hastened to the side of an Indian who had been gored by a bull. He inserted the man's protruding intestines back into his abdomen to save his life. Dr. Saler was a man of action who broke up quarrels among the citizens of Monterey as a wise piece of preventive medicine. One day he manhandled an irate citizen who was trying to knife the former military commandant, Hermengildo Sol.

Keeping the mission fathers healthy was one of the more difficult sides of the surgeon's practice. Dr. Juan de Dios Morelos of Monterey was called to the bedside of Father Puyal at Mission San Antonio in 1801. The father had been poisoned by his Indian missioners, and there was little the doctor could do. After death he performed an autopsy to reveal the unfortunate clergyman's black and putrid intestines. The Indians, thanking their savage gods for their success, poisoned other fathers in nearby San Miguel, but this time the fathers were hardier, the doctor more skilled, or the poison weaker, and the victims survived.

Sometimes the doctor helped to solve a murder mystery. Padre Andres Quintana was found dead in his cell, the holy oils and consecrated Host clasped to his breast. The matter was hushed up. Then two years later an old Indian on his deathbed said the father had been murdered under a tree and his corpse carried into the mission and placed in his own bed and his door locked from the inside. Dr. Manual Quixano hurried over from Monterey and performed an autopsy on the exhumed body which established that the father had been murdered in such a revolting way that he refused to give the details even to the court.

In 1805 a New Year's Day medical report to Spanish Viceroy Jose Marie Benites stated that the leading causes of death among the soldiers and settlers in California were dysentery, fevers, pleurisy, pneumonia, and venereal diseases. Dysentery, said Spanish doctors, was caused by using impure water in cooking food and the lack of individual cleanliness. Syphilis was rampant among the Indians, and the 1805 report said it was caused by "impure intercourse, filthy habits, sleeping huddled together, the sick with the others, the interchange of clothing, passing the nights in dancing and gambling, the unreasonable use of the temescal or sweat house from which perspiring freely, they jump into cold water."

The Indian sick frequently refused the aid of doctors because they were certain they were trying to kill them. There seems to be some evidence that their suspicion was justified. At least in Texas it is a matter of Spanish medical record that surgeons practiced difficult operations on sick Indians before undertaking surgery of a similar kind on whites.

Tuberculosis defied the doctors. They could do nothing to save a man already stricken with the disease, and few doctors gave any thought to how it was spread. Juan de Dios Morelos was convinced that it was infectious, and when Commandant Hermengildo Sol died at Monterey of consumption, he burned all his clothes and most of his furniture together with the roof, doors, and windows of his house. He had the floor bricks taken up and the plaster scraped from the walls in an effort to prevent the disease from infecting a new victim.

Spanish doctors had to hunt through the hills for herbs and roots from which to concoct many of the medicines they gave the sick. A scale for weighing ingredients was often the first thing for which a doctor sent back to Mexico or Spain. Doctors had to make their own instruments too. They attached a pig's bladder to a tube fashioned from an elder shoot to make a syringe. If a mother's milk failed, the doctor fitted a cow horn with a buckskin nipple to serve the baby as a nursing bottle.

Despite the strenuous efforts to eliminate smallpox, it continued to be the scourge of the frontier. In 1786, before Jenner announced his work on vaccination, a doctor in the Monterey area used vaccine derived from cowpox. In 1821 the Russian surgeon of the visiting ship *Kutusof* vaccinated fifty-four inhabitants. In 1844 American Consul Larkin in Monterey demonstrated to Californians that the United States also opposed smallpox. The Mexican schooner *California* had arrived in port with smallpox rampant among its Kanaka crew. The sick sailors remained on board ship, but their laundry was sent ashore. Eighty citizens soon died of the contagion, and a hospital was set up on the outskirts of town for the use of the poor and the sailors.

This pioneer hospital boasted two nurses and a burial squad, a practical feature indeed, for without doctors on the staff the patients died at a shocking rate. Finally Consul Larkin opened up his parlor to a dentist and an American mechanic named Streeter, who gave three hundred vaccinations. Fortunately they followed the example of Spanish court physician Xavier de Balmis and used virus obtained from healthy children. In Los Angeles a doctor undertook to vaccinate the population with vaccine taken from the dissolute Kanaka crew of the *Sterling*. He had a lot of explaining to do when many of his patients came down with syphilis.

Still farther south in San Diego it was up to James Ohio Pattie, a Kentucky trader, languishing in the calabozo, to stem the epidemic. He had come across the continent with his father in 1828 to trade with the Californians, but Governor Echeandra was suspicious of their intentions. He put them both in jail where the father died. Smallpox was raging, and Pattie had smallpox vaccine in his packs. He bargained with the governor to vaccinate the people if he would release him from his cell. The governor agreed, and trader Pattie vaccinated 22,000 persons before he ran out of serum. He won the friendship of the authorities, who offered him 500 mules and 500 cattle with land to graze them if he would become a Mexican citizen. Pattie refused and returned to the States.

The need to quarantine victims of the smallpox plague was evident, and hospitals were set up in garrison towns. On October 19, 1805, the Alamo in San Antonio was outfitted as a military infirmary. Patients slept on beds of reeds and were tended by male nurses, although women did the cooking. Dr. Frederico Zervan was the physician in charge. Dr. Zervan filled the Alamo with patients suffering from smallpox, pneumonia, influenza, gonorrhea, and syphilis. Soldiers injured in a fight with the Commanches near the Frio River were brought to the Alamo with arrow and bullet wounds.

An invoice dated April 2, 1807, lists a quantity of medical goods received at the Alamo. Judging by the drugs and devices included, it is apparent that medical practices in Spanish Texas were not too different from those on the Anglo-American frontier. There were seven boxes containing senna, sugar candy, cochineal, rhubarb, epsom salts, cinchona, incense, cream of tartar, Spanish fly, American ipecac, opium, borax, 3 dozen rubber bougies, 1 rubber catheter, tartar emetic, wine, spirits of scurvy grass, olive oil, frog cordial with mercury, simple cordial, divine cordial, a box of surgical instruments, 12 pointed Spanish lances, thin catgut, 2 large syringes, active mercury, corrosive, sublimate and sweet mercury, white arsenic and black bromide and 4 American cupping glasses.

The doctor armed with his seven boxes of medicines manfully

attacked disease and suffering. The governor helped by urging the soldiers to comb their hair daily and change their clothes once a week. Apparently Dr. Zervan's best efforts were not enough. Blunt Don Torivio Duran noted in his journal that the town's citizens "subject themselves to his prescriptions only through politeness and would rather subject themselves to Nature's remedies which work in favor of the individual than to those of a doctor whose ability they doubt."

When Dr. Zervan finally left for Chihuahua he forgot to repay forty-six bushels of corn he had borrowed from the government store and his estate was requisitioned. The official list showed the doctor's possessions to be: "An old bench, an organ with four cylinders out of order, four deteriorated portraits, one small box in which to keep coffee, one broken glass sconce, one old dragoon sword, one flat-iron for smoothing hats, one very much used checker board and one half sack of things that are not worth anything."

In this list there is a portrait of a lonely doctor on the frontier, surrounded by his few creature and aesthetic comforts, his checkerboard as his diversion, and a few steps away, the Alamo filled with the sick and the dying.

Throughout the Spanish and Mexican periods in the Southwest a doctor was rarely asked to show any other qualifications than a diploma, which to a half-illiterate alcalde need not necessarily be from a medical school. In the tradition of old Spain, barbers also did minor surgery and bled patients. Yldefonso Rey, such a barber-surgeon, arrived at San Antonio in 1785 and asked to be made the doctor. He informed the inhabitants that if each person would pay him two reales monthly, he would bleed them, shave them, and attend them and also their wives and children during any illness.

Rey's record as a healer was a good one, but elsewhere bleeders became so harmful, at least according to Governor Gorica of California, that it was necessary to outlaw them in 1799. With only a handful of bona fide doctors practicing in the whole

Southwest, citizens went right on asking the man who cut their hair to cut their flesh.

Hechiceros, or Indian medicine men, were also called upon in time of disease. They administered such herbs as yerba santa, which grew in the foothills, and a cathartic made from *cascara sagrada* bark and applied the leaves of the *grindelia* for afflictions as varied as poison oak and pneumonia.

Folk healers flourished in most of the settlements. Some of their practices were borrowed from the Aztecs of Mexico. For sore eyes the healer plastered the temple with a strange mess made from an Aztec receipe which called for white incense, earth of a decomposed corpse, all well ground up in dragon's blood and the white of an egg. Other folk salves and cures came from Spain or were invented by the settlers themselves. Santa Fe inhabitants rubbed cold olive oil on chigger bites. Everywhere the Spanish used maidenhair fern for blood disorders and applied unsalted lard mixed with sulphur, raw potato, roasted cactus leaves, and freshly killed chickens on open sores. They carried the eyetooth of a man or a black dog in the mouth to cure toothache and alleviated pleurisy by pressing a package of fresh horse manure steeped in wine against the chest.

A California folk healer who employed these obnoxious cures was hailed before a judge who threatened to expel him from the settlement as a quack. The man looked the judge straight in the eye and asked him to smell a herb, which he held out in his hand. The judge, returning his stare, coldly smelled the herb, and instantly broke into a copious nosebleed, which could not be stopped. At last the folk healer stepped forward and flicked a powder up the judge's nose. The bleeding stopped at once.

"This is the manner in which I cure my patients," said the healer.

The judge gave him his blessing to go home and practice medicine as he pleased.

In the early nineteenth century English, Irish, and Anglo-American doctors and medical adventurers turned up on the Spanish frontier. Twenty-one-year-old Dr. James William Burroughs of New York arrived in Santa Barbara in 1823. Californians found his name hard to pronounce so called him Diego Baris; they had no difficulty in appreciating his value as between the hours of nine and five he daily trudged from presidio to mission to fifty to sixty dwellings in the vicinity tending illnesses and accidents.

Apparently Dr. Burroughs did not practice long, because in 1829, when Alfred Robinson arrived in the town he found no doctor there. Robinson did find a woman in great abdominal pain and suggested a few drops of laudanum. When she immediately felt better, his reputation as a medico was made. Robinson had never received any medical training, but he at least could feel superior to another American who soon was practicing medicine in a nearby town. The latter was only an American sailor who had deserted a whaling ship and could scarcely write his name. The sailor, for his part, could feel superior to American William Money of Los Angeles who told his patients, as proof of his medical talents, "I was born with four teeth and with the likeness of a rainbow in my right eye."

Among the most reckless medical adventurers from the States was John Marsh, who firmly believed his bachelor's degree from Harvard University, Class of 1823, entitled him to practice medicine. He read some medicine before settling in Wisconsin where he was employed to help keep the Sioux at peace. He had to flee when authorities learned he was selling firearms to the very Indians he was supposed to pacify.

Traveling west over the Sante Fe Trail, Marsh was captured by Indians. As they were about to put him to death, he saw that the chief needed medical help. He treated the chief and was spared. He arrived in Los Angeles on New Year's Day 1836 and showed his Harvard diploma to the town council. Freely translating the Latin phrases to suit his purpose, he overawed the alcaldes into licensing him to practice medicine. His ranchero patients paid him in cowhides, which he sold for $500 and went north to start a ranch of his own.

Richard Somerset Den, a sheepskin doctor from Ireland, also

practiced in early Los Angeles. Don Ricardo, with an Irishman's flare for costume, rode a coal-black charger and dressed completely in black right down to a black felt hat and a large black scarf around his neck to set off his wavy white hair. Californians, who enjoyed good theater, approved and made him chief physician and surgeon of the Mexican Army, which futilely tried to defend them against the American invasion during the Mexican War. Dr. Den also bought a ranch, and he became wealthy.

An Englishman, Dr. Edward Turner Bale, who arrived at Monterey in 1837, eschewed dramatic dress in favor of a dramatic life. He decided the best way to establish a medical practice was to marry Governor Vallejo's niece, and so he did. To the ire of Californians the governor made him surgeon general.

Dr. Bale might have prospered if he had confined himself to medicine, but he soon opened a drugstore in a room rented from U. S. Consul Larkin. The drugstore metamorphosed into a saloon. One day while the doctor was drinking up some of his "drugstore" profits, the doughty governor returned from a fight with the Indians and received a hero's buss from Bale's wife. Bale angrily challenged Vallejo to a duel with swords.

Governor Vallejo, a celebrated swordsman, pinked the doctor unmercifully as the latter repeatedly rushed him. Seeing that he could not wound his agile opponent, Bale pulled out a pistol and shot at him. He was as poor a shòt as he was a swordsman, and he missed. To the governor this was simply no way for a gentlemen to behave, and he clapped the doctor in jail.

Only the comely Mrs. Bale's pleading obtained his release. The doctor gave up his medical practice and went into lumbering. On July 4, 1847, Englishman Edward Turner Bale made a final public exhibition of his flare for drama. To the surprised delight of American residents and the anger of Mexican authorities, he imbibed too much wine and sang "The Star-Spangled Banner" at the top of his voice.

Very likely drunken Dr. Bale revealed the political leanings of most of the Anglo-Saxon doctors and medical adventurers in the

Southwest. At least in Texas seven of the fifty-nine men who signed the Declaration of Independence from Mexico were doctors, and doctors Pollard, Thompson, and Michison died in the defense of the Alamo.

Chapter VII

BODIES AND SOULS

The doctor rode out from the Oregon mission post of Waiilatpu, meaning the place of the rye grass. He cantered his horse in the shadow of Blue Mountain until he came to the Cayuse village of Chief Tilaukait, his enemy. Smallpox had come riding home with a war party returning from a raid into California. The 1847 emigrant train had brought measles over the Oregon Trail to Waiilatpu Mission. It too had spread to the Cayuse village. Now the doctor rode to the Indian camp to treat the men, women, and children, who huddled in their teepees, clawed their pustules and burned with fever with only a few gaunt squaws trying to care for them all. He found twenty-five sick to a teepee. Women and children turned their faces from him in fear. Men stared at him with hatred despite their nearness to death.

Marcus Whitman was a missonary doctor. The sickness of the souls he saw before him appalled him as much as the sickness of the bodies. Even as he set about applying his cures, making this sufferer more comfortable, dispensing a soothing salve there, he knew that his mission had been a failure. Instead of Christian love around him he saw hatred.

It seemed a long twelve years since in the glory of May he had first started up the Missouri River with Fontenelle's Brigade of trappers. The first night on the trail the trappers had got drunk and pelted the Reverend Samuel Parker and himself with rotten eggs. What a preposterous figure the minister had made in his schoolmaster's coat and plug hat! He was a certain target for a mountain man's spite. The Reverend Parker had done little to help the caravan on its way, while Whitman helped to build rafts and rude bridges so that the wagons and mules could cross tributary streams.

When the brigade reached Bellevue, cholera struck. Suddenly overpowered by the strange and terrifying disease, the men sprawled on the river bank in their own excrement. On June 10, the doctor diagnosed his first case. Not many frontier doctors at that time would have recognized the symptoms, but he had read articles about cholera when the disease had appeared in eastern cities in the year before. He realized that immediate steps must be taken to isolate the stricken men from those still healthy. In the morning the mountain men had been playing crude tricks on him; in the afternoon they did exactly as he said because they were afraid. They erected shelters on the river bluffs and carried the sick men to them. Fontenelle was stricken, but Whitman nursed him back to health. One night the doctor himself was so ill he could not go to a dying man. Yet of fifty-odd men in the brigade only three died.

Fontenelle's Brigade had at last crossed the high pass of the Continental Divide and dropped down to the hidden rendezvous on the banks of the Green River. There in the purity of God's wilderness Whitman found corruption. Mountain men had come from all points of the compass to drink, dance and quarrel, lust after dusky squaws, race their horses, and gamble. The doctor looked upon it all with the eyes of a man who would not even drink whiskey. Once reveling trappers seized him and tried to force the contents of a bottle between his clenched teeth. He stubbornly insisted that they could hold his head under water, but he still would not let a swallow pass his throat.

The day after his arrival he probed Jim Bridger's back for a Blackfoot arrowhead. Fortified by formidable drafts of whiskey, Bridger bit on a piece of wood as the doctor's knife dug into his flesh. Indians and trappers watched and jostled one another. They were so impressed that Whitman was kept busy for the rest of the rendezvous digging old bullets and arrowheads from their tough hides.

A stubborn, pious man, with proud blue eyes and a large determined mouth, Marcus Whitman was a match for the trappers, just as now, years later in Tilaukait's Cayuse village, he was a match for the hatred of the Indians. His kind hands passed over them, bringing healing where healing was possible. He rode away leaving behind medicines for smallpox and measles. He did not look back to see some of the Indians spit after him and pour the medicine into the fires.

"The doctor seeks only to poison us so that the whites can have our lands," said old Chief Tilaukait.

The chief had already lost two sons to smallpox, and a third was sick. When the doctor was gone, the chief placed the boy in a teepee and steamed him by throwing water on rocks heated in the fire. This was the Cayuse cure. Then he dropped him naked into the icy river to kill the disease. The severe treatment brought death quickly to the child, and the old chief stood distracted before his teepee. His greasy black hair, his gnarled cheeks, and his stumpy teeth made a mask of grief.

As the doctor rode back to his mission on the river bank, his thoughts seemed more real than the wilderness valley about him. The man of action had become a man of introspection, remembering the hardships and savoring the exaltation of the past.

As he drew close to the three buildings of the mission, an auburn-haired woman appeared at the doorway of his house, the doorway he himself had carved. The doctor brightened with the expectancy of homecoming. Unsaddling his horse, he fed him grain and turned him into the corral. He carried saddle, blanket, and bridle to the blacksmith shop and hung them on a peg beneath the eaves. Only then did he go into his house to take his seat in one of the chairs he had made and listen to the melodious voice of his auburn-haired Narcissa.

Always Narcissa had been an exceptional girl in the upstate New York towns where her father had been a judge. In another place and time she would have been called a bluestocking, for she was purposeful and superior in intellect. She had fallen in love both with the idea of going to Oregon as a missionary and with Marcus Whitman. Their austere romance led to a strange wedding. The doctor had returned from his first trip into the West. In the Presbyterian Church at Angelica, Narcissa appeared in a wedding dress of black bombazine. The bridegroom entered with an Indian boy from the West, a heathen child in this white man's church. To close the service the congregation sang bravely:

"In the deserts let me labor,
On the mountains let me tell,
How He died—the blessed Savior—
To redeem the world from hell!"

The voices sobbed with emotion. One by one the singers stopped singing to weep at the "going forth" to come so soon after the wedding. Only Narcissa sang on, her voice sweet and strong.

"Let me hasten,
Far in heathen lands to dwell."

The Indian boy looked on it all with opaque black eyes. Soon the young missionary couple were on a riverboat steaming west. Then they traveled by wagon with a party across the high prairies to the mountains.

As she set the table in the mission house, Narcissa's face was seamed with hardship and trouble. During the crossing of the prairies her cheeks had been soft, her eyes still softer, as she baked bread in the open for her husband, made forks from sticks, brewed tea over the flames kindled with dried buffalo dung, and learned to relish boiled buffalo tongue and broiled hump steak. Marcus and Narcissa forded streams without fear. The doctor, already half a mountain man, showed her how he spread himself on a buffalo robe, grasped the edges, and floated across. She did not dare attempt such a dangerous crossing. Drifting down the Columbia in the Oregon, which she loved from the first time the word sounded in her ears, Narcissa had gone ashore at a spot where the Indians yearly fished a rapids for salmon. She had blundered into a nest of fleas left from their recent encampment. Laughing, the doctor had helped her pursue the tormentors. Finally she had sheltered behind a big rock, taken off her clothing, and one by one captured her unwelcome companions.

The doctor built his mission only twenty-six miles from the Hudson's Bay Company's Fort Walla Walla. Cayuse tribesmen helped him to log the timber and handsaw it into lumber in a pit. There were two bedchambers, a kitchen, and a pantry beneath a slanting roof of mud and boughs. There was neither bed nor table, but Narcissa threw herself down on the floor before a fire in the fireplace and laughed with joy. Marcus and she had a home. By February 18, 1837, the first anniversary of their marriage, the spring had melted away the snow of the first winter on the Walla Walla. Whitman made chairs and prepared to plow. Then on March 14, the evening of Narcissa's twenty-ninth birthday, Alice Clarissa came, the first white child to be born in the territory.

Two years passed with the planting, the harvesting and the sleeping time of winter. The Cayuse showed little inclination to accept the white man's complex God and even less inclination to accept the white man's burden of farm work. As a youth Whitman had ridden beside Dr. Ira Bryant, cousin of the poet William Cullen Bryant, to north-country log camps and cabins to dispense simple remedies and help the doctor set broken bones. In 1825 he had studied at the Medical College at Fairfield, New York, and practiced in Pennsylvania, Ontario, and New York before he had felt the call to Oregon. Here in the country of the Cayuse he gave out calomel and iodine, bled patients, and applied blisters when needed. He knew little of antisepsis and nothing of anesthesia, but he was the first American doctor in the Northwest.

On almost every Sabbath day the Whitmans sang "Rock of Ages" for the Cayuse. Then they settled down to read.

"Supper is almost ready," said precocious two-year-old Alice one Sunday as her parents read. "Let Alice get some water."

The parents hardly looked up from their books as she left. The afternoon shadows lengthened. A mission workman interrupted to say he had seen two of the household cups floating on the river waters. Should he get a pole and fish them out?

"No, let them be," replied the doctor. "Get them out tomorrow. This is the Sabbath."

The father and mother continued to read. Suddenly Narcissa let her book fall and cried out. She flung herself through the door and hurried to the river bank, where she ran up and down. An old Cayuse, knee-deep in swirling waters, was fishing in the river. He bent over and lifted the body of a small white child from beneath the surface.

Desperately the doctor tried artificial respiration, but it was too late. Narcissa could only take her dead child and say, "Lord, it is right. She is not mine, but thine." Whitman built a coffin and placed their daughter in it. They buried her in a grave on the plain within sight of their doorstep.

From then on the life of the mission began to decay. Narcissa's eyes at thirty-two were failing from sewing and reading by candlelight. The doctor's face became leathery; his back and side ached. He walked with a limp. Still he rode on his medical rounds; still he sought to save bodies and souls.

The doctor planted his corn by the river, and Chief Tilaukait turned his horses loose in the unfenced field. When the doctor sent mission Indians to remove them, the chief told him bitterly, "I put the horses in the corn because that is an easy way to keep them from straying out and getting lost."

"I thought our field was a plantation, not a horse pen," said the doctor meekly, "but if you think it is well for your horses to eat our crops I have nothing more to say."

The chief had no understanding of such meekness.

"This is my land," he cried in anger. "I grew to a man here. The horses eat only what comes up out of my land. What have you ever paid me for the land?"

They spoke together in Chinook jargon and the Nez Perce language. The doctor admitted he had paid nothing.

"Are you not ashamed?" demanded the chief.

"Wait now while I speak," replied the doctor, his own anger

rising. "We did not come here of ourselves. We were invited. And the land was given to us."

He turned and walked away. Seizing him by the shoulder, the chief spun him around and punched his fist twice against the doctor's chest.

"You talk too much. Stop talking," he screamed, as the doctor staggered back.

"I have been talking since I was a child, and I will not stop now."

Perplexed and angry, the chief strode away, and his perplexity and anger turned to hatred as he brooded in his teepee. When William Gray, a blunt assistant, turned an Indian out of the mission kitchen, he went to the corral and took a horse. Gray stopped him. He went away angrily. Soon Tilaukait appeared with a crowd of angry Cayuse to demand an explanation. A brave pulled one of Whitman's ears. The doctor turned his head in response to his Master's interdict, and the Indian pulled the other ear. He threw the doctor's hat in the mud. Whitman asked a friendly Indian to pick it up and put it on his head. It dripped mud and water down his seamed face.

"Perhaps you are playing," he said to the chief.

The Indians went away. Now Archibald McKinlay, the Hudson's Bay Company representative at Fort Walla Walla, took a hand. He informed the Indians that they had acted like dogs. Stung by the insult, Tilaukait returned to the mission again with a band of tribesmen. They burst into the kitchen and stormed through the rooms. Narcissa barred the kitchen door against reinforcements from the mob milling in the mission yard. An old man smashed one of her precious windows with a hammer and demanded that she let him in. Inside the mission, Indians rushed about tumbling furniture, overturning cases of medical supplies. With hammer and ax those outside smashed the kitchen door down and rushed in.

Dr. Whitman and William Gray tried to parley with the chief in the dining room. An old brave named Pelaistiwat and a young buck called Tomahas rushed toward them. Tomahas brandished a hammer at Gray, who wrenched the weapon away. Pelaistiwat lunged at Whitman with an ax. Seeing that the chief had no intention of stopping the attack, the doctor seized the ax from the old man. Pelaistiwat tore Whitman's coat and struck him in the mouth in his impotent rage. The Indians in the room whooped with glee. Tomahas took a war club from a friend and struck at Whitman, who dodged and grabbed hold. Again the Indians whooped. At last the white doctor had lost his meekness and was defending himself against death.

"I do not fear death," gasped the doctor as he struggled, "but I refuse the sin of letting it happen if I can prevent it."

Tomahas, losing his grip on the war club, took a rifle and pointed it at Whitman's heart. He was about to pull the trigger when two farm workers rushed into the room, armed with rifles. They covered the chief and Tomahas. The Indians withdrew from the mission and contented themselves with throwing stones at the remaining windows and at the farm animals.

During the winter of 1842–43 Whitman rode through blizzards and the threat of Indian attacks over a route which stretched an incredible 4000 miles, as far south as Taos and Santa Fe and east through Kansas to Westport. He sought to persuade the American Mission Board in Boston not to dismantle Waiilatpu. Then he returned over the Oregon Trail with 1000 settlers on their way to the Willamette Valley. When he was near to the end of the trail, he hurried ahead to find his gristmill burned by the Indians, the mission windows and doors broken, and farm equipment smashed. Narcissa had gone to the Methodist mission at the Dalles. As he went to the Dalles to bring back Narcissa, the advance guard of the settlers reached Waiilatpu and sacked it again, causing as much damage as had the Indians.

Limping on his bad leg, fearful that his wan Narcissa suffered from an "aneurism of the main aorta below the heart," Whitman returned to the place of the rye grass. There he fed the ever mounting tide of settlers. He took in the strays and the orphans to his haven in the wilderness. The Indians saw the doctor helping the thousands of whites passing through their country on the way to more favored lands farther west, and their hatred for him deepened. The whites were taking away their country.

On the drizzling day after he had returned from Tilaukait's village, the doctor who was reading in his Bible, heard a knock on the door. It was an Indian known as Green Cap hunching in his blanket against the cold.

"A son of Tilaukait is dead," he said. "He is being taken to the burial grounds now."

"We will go together," said the doctor, getting into his coat.

At the funeral the doctor found only the old chief, sullen with grief at the loss of his last son, and his relatives. Strangely enough, there were no other Cayuse. The doctor returned late from the burial grounds. He finished his dinner by two o'clock and then went up the steep stairway to where a sick woman lay. Narcissa was giving some of the orphaned children taken from wagon trains a hot bath in the kitchen when he came back downstairs. He went to his medicine cabinet to prepare a remedy.

In the kitchen Mary Ann, the dark, beautiful daughter of Jim Bridger, started to wash the dishes. Young John Sager sat down near her to make a broom and talk. Ten-year-old Elizabeth Sager, first in the tub, asked Narcissa for a glass of milk, and she indulgently stepped into the pantry to draw a cupful from the bottom spout of a separator pan. She turned back to the kitchen and stopped so suddenly the milk dashed from the cup. Tilaukait and Tomahas stood within the door. Quickly she slipped into the sitting room, slammed shut the door and bolted it.

"Doctor, you are wanted by Tilaukait and Tomahas," she said.

Calmly the doctor opened the door and went into the kitchen. "Lock the door after me," he cautioned.

Tilaukait talked. He wanted medicine for the sickness in his lodge. The doctor looked at him, still trying to find a measure of love in his enemy's scowling face. The old man had lost another son. Would grief soften his heart or harden it further? The doctor did not see Tomahas drop his blanket and swing the pipe tomahawk. The dull blade struck his grizzled head. John Sager sprang for a loaded pistol hanging on the wall, but Tilaukait lifted a rifle from beneath his blanket and dropped him to the floor with one shot. He quickly drew a knife and cut the boy's throat. Whitman was dazed, but he managed to stagger to the outside door and open it before the tomahawk struck again. He reeled out of doors, slipped in the mud and fell to his knees. Tilaukait reloaded. Pressing the muzzle of his gun to the doctor's throat, he pulled the trigger. When the doctor slumped forward into the mud, the Indians swarmed into the mission, killing and plundering. Narcissa died soon after her husband. The place of the rye grass, intended to be a medical mission in the Oregon wilderness, smelled of massacre and death.

Chapter VIII

MILITARY SURGEONS

General Howard's troops struck Chief Joseph's Nez Perce warriors on the Clearwater River of Idaho in 1877 and were badly mauled. At the end of the day the soldiers were pinned down behind sheltering rocks by Indian snipers, who fired from cover a scant hundred yards away. Every movement brought an Indian bullet whining out of the dusk.

When twilight faded, Surgeon George Miller Sternberg and an aide crawled out onto the battlefield looking for the wounded. They crept so close to the enemy that they could hear the Indians talking, but by then the dark night hid them. Close to the army lines the doctor found a wounded soldier. His deft fingers located an artery pulsing blood. Already the man had lost so much blood that the doctor knew that if he moved him he would die. The bleeding must be stopped on the darkened battlefield with the Indians ready to fire at any suspicious sound or movement.

Dr. Sternberg whispered instructions to his aide, who held a blanket to screen the wounded man from the view of the Indians. He lit a candle so that the doctor could see as he tied the artery. Peering into the night, an Indian made out a ghostly glow on the battlefield; it was the candle hidden behind the heavy army blanket. Was it a spirit rising from a dead soldier? He held his fire, but finally as the doctor was suturing the vessel, he shot at the mysterious light. The bullet nipped the candle out, and the doctor, thrown into darkness, had to finish the operation by touch. Then the aide and he gently and stealthily carried the soldier to the army lines.

All evening Indian snipers had been picking off thirsty soldiers as they wormed on their bellies toward a bubbling spring some distance from the lines.

"For God's sake bring us water to drink," cried the wounded, as Dr. Sternberg dressed one man's shattered leg, another man's punctured abdomen, and dug bullets from tortured flesh. Finally the doctor called a few brave men to him and asked them to go with him and bring water to the wounded. The doctor and his party, keeping their canteens from rattling, edged forward through the night until they were able to dip them into the spring. They brought water back to quench the thirst of the suffering men.

Several of the wounded died during the night, although Dr. Sternberg moved sleeplessly among them, changing dressings and giving drugs. Twenty-seven seriously hurt men were still alive in the morning. The Indians had slipped away into the mountains. The beleaguered men shouted with relief and triumph, but Dr. Sternberg was lost in his thoughts. How could he transport the wounded men twenty-five miles to Grangeville, the nearest settlement? He had no ambulance wagons; he had no litters. In decamping the Indians had left behind a number of long lodge poles, and Dr. Sternberg's eyes came to rest on them. He fastened a frame of boughs between two long poles to make a travois. The top ends of the poles were tied to two sides of a horse; the bottom dragged over the ground. A sick man was strapped to the load-bearing frame. He made as many travois as there were wounded.

On the trail the doctor, his aide riding at his side, followed behind the wounded. He noted with grim satisfaction that the flexible poles climbed easily over the rocks to give the men much more comfortable rides than if they rode in a jolting ambulance. From time to time the column stopped so that the doctor could change dressings. Once he amputated a leg. Worn out with the battle, the night of caring for the casualties, and the agonized journey, the doctor threatened to topple from his horse. His aide shouted to help keep him awake and grabbed him every time he began to fall to the ground. At last Dr. Sternberg arrived at Grangeville. Only two men had died on the trail.

Doctors who fought side by side with cavalry and foot soldiers in the fierce Indian wars were accustomed to sharing their hardships and dangers. The first U. S. Army medical officer ever to be killed in battle was killed fighting Indians. He was Surgeon's Mate Victor Grasson, and he was shot down during St. Clair's defeat on the Maumee River in Ohio in 1791. As a matter of Department of Army record, the first soldier ever to win the Congressional Medal of Honor was also a military surgeon, Bernard John Dowling Irwin, and he received the coveted award for his exploits in a campaign against Cochise in 1861.

Other army doctors in the Indian wars showed bravery and medical skill. Dr. George Martin Kober fought with the troops in the Modoc Wars of Oregon. In the eerie Battle of the Lava Beds, bullets richocheted among the brittle rocks of a face-of-the-moon landscape. Dr. Kober and a young physician, John O. Skinner, set up a dressing station behind a ridge which was less than waist high. Every time the doctors, picking out shattered bones and suturing gaping wounds, made the mistake of appearing over the ridge, the Indians showered bullets on them. Dr. Kober patched up one man and taught Dr. Skinner, who had never before performed an operation, how to stanch the flow of blood from a bullet-severed main artery in the arm of another. Even when he was struck in the arm by a bullet, he treated the wounded before he allowed Dr. Skinner to come to his relief.

Doctors also rode into battle halfway across the continent on the Great Plains frontier. At Bates Creek on July 4, 1874, Dr. Thomas Maghee's forehead was creased by a Sioux bullet as he dressed a soldier's wound. Here is the War Department version.

"While dressing the wound of Private Gable, he was the object of the direct fire of an Indian, partly hidden in a ravine, until, laying down his instruments for a moment, he took his carbine and, stepping out a few paces, killed the Indian and then returned quietly to his work."

One of the most colorful of the soldier doctors was Valentine McGillycuddy—Dr. "Gillycuddy" as Calamity Jane always called him. When he arrived at Fort Laramie, Calamity, then a young girl orphaned by the Indians, came to his quarters.

"How-do, Dr. 'Gillycuddy,'" she said.

He invited her to sit down on a chair, but instead she sat on the ground. Grinning, the doctor sat on the ground too and immediately won her friendship.

Soon after his arrival, Dr. McGillycuddy mounted a beautiful black horse provided by the horse sergeant and started off across the plains. Troopers sniggered to each other as they watched the tenderfoot mount and ride away. Suddenly the horse bolted. McGillycuddy sawed on the bit until the animal's mouth bled, but the loco horse streaked toward a slack telegraph line. The wire whipped the doctor's hat off. Still he alternately cursed and gentled the horse to a docile trot. Calamity cantered up to him and admitted that the sergeant had given him the worst mount in the regiment.

"Just because he thought you was a city guy who didn't know how to ride," she said. "They heard y' swear and they seen y' pat the horse and talk friendly to him and they know now y' ain't just a city guy."

Calamity Jane volunteered to nurse Dr. McGillycuddy's patients. She stayed up nights caring for the sick. On most military posts in the West, nursing was done by soldiers who were detailed for the duty in the same way they were given guard duty or ordered to dig latrines. At Fort Laramie, Dr. McGillycuddy came to rely on the girl, and he regretted leaving her behind at the fort when the troopers took to the field.

Later, as Dr. McGillycuddy rode with a wagon train of supplies to General George Crook's camp on the Rosebud River of Montana, Indian smoke signals warned of their progress. At night the doctor slept on one of the stretchers he was taking with him into the fighting, and the soldiers, who were billeted on the hard ground, were envious. One night he snapped awake to the sound of gunshots. Bullets whistled through his tent. He rolled off the stretcher and slept belly tight on the ground from then on.

"Sleep well?" grinned a soldier in the morning.

Sitting Bull's men had shot up the camp and fled.

Dr. McGillycuddy reported to General Crook and soon rode out with the 2nd Cavalry. Bands of Indians knifed in and out of the army lines. Dr. McGillycuddy was in the thick of the fighting. After the Indians withdrew, the doctor and the stretcher-bearers went up and down the battlefield gathering the wounded. When the doctor completed bandaging a man with blood streaming from his face, he noticed a soldier kneeling beside a log, still watching for Indians, his gun still aimed.

"Put down your gun; the battle's over," he said.

The soldier didn't move. Going up to him, the doctor found his body stiff to the touch and then saw a bullet had pierced his left eye.

On the trail Dr. McGillycuddy brought up the rear, keeping the sick from falling behind. Once he found a Lieutenant Huntington doubled up with cramps. He gave him a dose of morphine, but by the time the rear guard passed, the lieutenant still could not move. Bravely he urged the doctor to leave him, but Dr. McGillycuddy cut saplings, made a travois, and dragged the sick man along the trail left by the Army. He caught up with the cavalry that night.

"Who goes there?" challenged a sentry on the camp perimeter.

"The wounded train," replied the doctor.

A fighting surgeon in the field was cut off from fresh medical supplies, and before he left the fort he made sure that he carried what he needed with him. Dr. Kober, outfitting for an expedition into southeastern Nevada to punish Indians who had killed a miner, noted that he packed: "instruments, medicines, surgical dressings, splints, hospital stores, litters, blankets, mattresses, horse-hair pillows packed in panniers, blanket cases and two special field chests."

Surgeon James Kimball carried a mess table with him on one campaign. After a battle he amputated mutilated limbs on it. Then he washed the blood off and calmly sat down to the table to eat his dinner. Dr. Kimball also improvised a litter on wheels that would have intrigued Rube Goldberg. Faced with transporting an officer wounded by the Sioux over rough virgin prairie, he placed the injured man on canvas stretched between two pairs of wheels. A mule drew the contraption over the plains.

Even when a wounded trooper reached the fort, the doctor was hard put to save his life with the skimpy medical supplies and equipment he had at his command. In the 1870s at Fort Washakie in Wyoming, Surgeon William Arthur stretched a wounded soldier out on a mess table he had borrowed from the barracks. The man had been shot in the leg. Gangrene had set in. A hemorrhage in the middle of the night had brought the doctor running to the sick ward. He saw he had to amputate at the hip joint. Here is his terse account:

"By the light of a few candles, the operation was done. The anesthetic was given by the hospital cook, a private of cavalry. The hospital steward, recently appointed, fainted at the first stab of the knife, was shoved under a bed and left to come to in his own good time. A patient in the ward, a cavalry private, crawled out of bed, told me he had worked in a drug store before enlisting and offered to help; he did very well, and the disarticulation was soon completed."

The patient died before daybreak. When the bugle sang the morning sick call, Surgeon Arthur scrutinized the ailing soldiers, issued this one a pill, gave that one a dose. Sick call was routine at the more than two hundred military posts scattered through the trans-Missouri West in the middle decades of the nineteenth century, but even so a doctor could not let the night's ordeal lessen his vigilance, for he never knew when he would spot the first symptoms of scurvy or cholera. He was well acquainted with the old adage that ten men in war died of disease for every one killed by the enemy. He knew that the greatest foes a soldier had to face never put on war paint and set an ambush by a river crossing. They were cholera, scurvy, yellow fever, tuberculosis, and typhoid fever.

Cholera, which Dr. Daniel Drake had observed marching with General Scott's troops to the Black Hawk War, marched ever westward with the soldiers. Late in the summer of 1855 the disease broke out at Fort Riley, Kansas, where Major Edmund A. Ogden was in command. Within twenty-four hours after the first case, several troopers were dead and dozens more were screaming with pain. Over a hundred soldiers, including Assistant Surgeon James Simmons were terrified by the disease and ran away into the hills. Major Ogden, sick himself, nursed his men until on the third day he died. That day fourteen others also died; fifty more were stricken. Men fell sick at noon and were dead before the dawn. A brave but ignorant civilian doctor from nearby Manhattan burned barrels of pine tar beneath the open windows of the fort hospital, but the soldiers still died at the rate of seventy-five to one hundred a week.

The cholera spread. At Fort Zarah, Kansas, a survivor remembered later that "Men were seized with cramping of the stomach, bowels and muscles of the arms and legs." By midmorning of the first day five at Fort Zarah were dead, and thirty-six were sprawled on the parade ground too sick to move.

The plague besieged Fort Harker, Kansas, and there Dr. George Sternberg encountered it for the first time. It was in 1867. An acting assistant surgeon had been called to the quarters of the fort herder, who had collapsed. The doctor observed with horror that the sick man's bowels were discharging rice-water stools. The herder writhed with cramps; his fingers were shriveled and bone hard. Twelve hours later he was dead. The epidemic was raging by the time Dr. Sternberg arrived. The surgeon cared for the stricken, but he made his greatest efforts to protect the healthy. He noted that the camp policing was not good; the latrines were in filthy condition. He slushed out the barracks with disinfectants and demanded that the men wash often and keep their clothing clean. Let a soldier get the slightest diarrhea, and the doctor routed him from his tent and isolated him in the hospital tent. He warned all personnel not to bathe in the Smoky Hill River or drink its water.

Dr. Sternberg won his battle against cholera. At last he had only one more case to report to Surgeon General Barnes in Washington.

"One of the ladies of the garrison died of cholera on the 15th. of July," he wrote.

He did not add that the lady was his own young bride, who had ridden out from the East anticipating an exciting life on the frontier with her doctor husband.

Scurvy rivaled cholera in its lethal attacks on soldiers. The 6th Infantry Regiment and the 2nd Battalion of the New Hampshire Rifle Regiment ascended the Missouri on the first steamboat to navigate the treacherous muddy waters. On September 26, 1819, they landed at a site above modern Omaha and established a fort. The soldiers settled down with enough salt meat, flour and Indian corn meal to last the winter.

At first game was plentiful, but as blizzards howled down the river valley, wild animals disappeared. The men had no fresh vegetables or meat, and by January 560 of the 788 soldiers were sick with scurvy. One hundred and fifty-seven died before April, when the two army surgeons, Thomas G. Mower and John Gale, were able to dig enough wild onions from the thawing earth to keep the sick alive. A relief force drove a herd of cattle overland from Fort Osage, bringing fresh meat, milk, and butter to the garrison, which had been dying for lack of vitamin C.

As the decades passed, military surgeons on the frontier came to realize that it was the soldier's diet of meat, white bread, soda biscuits, hardtack, syrup, lard, and black coffee, which caused the livid spots, the swollen and bleeding gums, and the prostration of scurvy. During the construction of the Walla Walla Military Road in Montana, Captain John Mullan in command of the detachment noted, "with regard to the scurvy that among civilian employees who received five days' fresh beef and two days' dessicated vegetables out of the seven, not a single symptom appeared, every case being confined to the soldiers, who received but two days' fresh beef and two days' dessicated vegetables in the seven."

The captain's brother, Dr. James A. Mullan, was surgeon with the force. He brought the twenty-five scurvy victims back to health with the help of fresh vegetables and vinegar. Elsewhere military surgeons scoured the countryside in search of wild fruits and vegetables that would ward off the disease. Dr. William S. Latta, surgeon of the 2nd Nebraska Cavalry, campaigning in the Dakotas in 1863, had the men gather wild gooseberries to make a stew. In Texas military surgeons variously gave soldiers fresh agave juice, prickly pear, pokeweed, and wild lamb's-lettuce. Many doctors turned gardener in their fight against scurvy. They grew tomatoes for the most part, but Dr. James Kimball at Fort Wingate, New Mexico, instead irrigated the desert and tended cabbages and kohlrabi. He had the cook prepare a health-giving sauerkraut picked from his fields.

Yellow fever was just as deadly as scurvy and cholera but not nearly as widespread. At Fort Brown, Texas, on the Mexican border, in 1853 Surgeon S. P. Moore reported 245 cases and 50 deaths. He also claimed that yellow fever was a distinctive disease and tried without success to treat it with nitric acid and salt in place of quinine. Twenty-nine years later another young surgeon arrived at Fort Brown, and there he also had his first brush with yellow fever. His name was William Crawford Gorgas.

That year the fever had started in Mexican Matamoros. Next there were a few cases at the fort, first thought to be dengue, then break-bone fever, then spectral yellow fever itself. Soldiers said it was the wind bringing the odor of oranges and bananas from Mexico that carried the yellow death on its wings. They drank whiskey and munched on mustard seed to ward it off, and they buried a man as fast as he died. There were 2300 cases in the border area around the fort.

The first night that young Gorgas spent at Fort Brown he sat late on the gallery with pretty Marie Doughty. She admired his soft southern drawl and his wit. At four in the morning she awoke burning with fever and called for the young doctor. When he arrived at her bedside, she handed him her fan.

"You fan me," she said.

Gorgas had never had yellow fever, nor had he ever seen a case, but he recognized his adversary at once and knew he was to be an implacable foe of the disease that threatened the life of this beautiful girl. He made Marie as comfortable as he could.

In the morning the commanding officer, fearing to lose his doctor to the disease, ordered Gorgas to stay out of the yellow-fever wards. Soon afterward, a young officer passing an open window in the dead room caught sight of the doctor dissecting the corpse of a new victim.

"Good morning, Captain!" called Gorgas. "Will you come in?"

The terrified captain fled and reported Gorgas to the commanding officer. As punishment for his breach of discipline, the surgeon was ordered to live in the infected part of the fort. He cared for the dying and took turns with a civilian doctor from Brownsville at reading burial services. One day as the two doctors buried the eighteen-year-old son of an officer, the civilian pointed to a fresh grave.

"This is Miss Doughty's grave. Will you read the burial service for her this afternoon?"

"Yes, I will read her burial service," said Gorgas quietly.

Marie Doughty was even then in the black-vomit stage. Yet somehow she survived. Dr. Gorgas himself was stricken; he wrestled against death, and he too won. Yellow fever now dropped its sallow mask to play cupid in one of the strangest courtships of the western frontier. Marie and the soft-spoken young doctor convalesced together. They walked among the hills to regain their strength. Dr. Gorgas spent hours reading Dickens and Thackeray to the sick men, and Marie sat in a chair, listening. One day he took her to the fort cemetery and showed her the grave that had been dug for her. Gorgas married the girl, and years later, when his life on the frontier was only a memory, he conquered yellow fever for all mankind.

Yellow fever, cholera, and scurvy breached the garrison's medical defenses and carried off soldiers by the scores. Other diseases slipped into the fort to kill one by one. These killers were as common as the grippe, tuberculosis, and pneumonia, or as rare as Rocky Mountain spotted fever. Garrison doctors fought them with medicines and methods that in the light of today's medical knowledge seem often to smack more of black magic than science.

Just as often the doctors displayed a remarkable if primitive insight into the nature of the sickness. Here are examples:

Fort Humboldt, Nevada. Sick call brought a twenty-year-old soldier with tuberculosis to Dr. George Martin Kober. The doctor directed that a beef be slaughtered every day and the youth be given a pint of its warm blood to drink. The soldier fully recovered.

Fort Clark, Texas. A soldier fell asleep in the sun, and a fly deposited its larvae in his nostrils. Dr. James B. Kimball chloroformed him and dug the maggots out of his nose.

Fort Gibson, Arkansas. Assistant Surgeon Charles McCormick treated pneumonia with sulphate of quinine.

Fort Totten, the Dakotas. Colonel William B. Davis, Medical Corps, noticed that grippe broke out every time there was a sack of mail from home and believed the germs must be transmitted by the Postal Department.

Camp Stanford, California. Assistant Surgeon John Kunkler attributed an outbreak of measles to fungi.

Fort Douglas, Utah. Dr. Charles Smart thought Rocky Mountain spotted fever was caused by a malarious poison contained in snow water. He cautioned soldiers against eating snow.

High winds in the Southwest blew dust into the eyes of men, and doctors treated them for ophthalmia. High winds in the mountains and on the Great Plains blew blizzards of snow at exposed forts, and doctors treated men for snow blindness and amputated frozen toes and fingers.

On the trail in the Dakotas in midwinter Dr. Valentine McGillycuddy directed soldiers to stamp circulation back into their feet, beat their hands together, and rub snow on frosted ears and noses. At night when the men camped in the freezing wind, the doctor passed a whiskey bottle around. During the day he kept the bottle locked up in his medical-supply locker, and the key in his pocket. Things went well on this expedition; only one man froze to death, although before the force reached Fort Robinson every officer and man was frostbitten.

With the temperature sometimes dropping to fifty below zero

on the northern plains, the doctor himself was in danger of freezing as he made his medical rounds. Dr. James Kimball described his winter dress while at Fort Buford in the Dakotas as follows:

"First a pair of buffalo overshoes—buffalo hide with the hair on, making a shoe about two inches thick all around, thus adding four inches in length and four inches in breadth to my natural foot; gloves reaching nearly to my shoulders, woolen and lined with deerskin, a shaggy buffalo overcoat and bearskin leggins. My cap is made from a beaver's skin and is the respectable feature of my outlandish outfit."

Military doctors not only tended the sick and bound up the wounds of the injured but by order of the Secretary of War they also studied the weather, geology, plants, fauna, Indian customs, and antiquities. They were such eager collectors that the Army Medical Museum in Washington is filled with mementos of their tours of duty in the Old West. Dr. James Kimball exchanged a dollar and fifty cents' worth of provisions with a Yankton Sioux for a complete autobiography of Sitting Bull in Indian picture writing. It is a priceless work set down on muster-roll blanks stolen by the Indians from the 31st U. S. Infantry. George Miller Sternberg, stationed at Fort Walla Walla, Washington, in 1876, rode out on fossil hunts in hostile Indian territory. He brought back excellent specimens of prehistoric horse, elephant, camel, elk, and deer.

Some of the military doctors' medical findings proved of great importance. Dr. George Miller Sternberg studied French so that he could read Pasteur. In 1881 he discovered pneumococcus, the cause of lobar pneumonia, in his own sputum, only a few months after the great Frenchman first isolated the bacteria. Today many doctors acclaim Sternberg, who later became Surgeon General in Washington, as the father of American bacteriology.

When Surgeon Albert J. Myer rode with the cavalry across the Texas plains in the 1850s, Indian smoke signals and beacon lights meant more to him than that the redskins were keeping an eye on army movements. Studying the Indians' communication methods, he devised his own system of signaling with flags by

6. Mountain men
who trapped for furs in the Far West
learned the skills of the Indian medicine lodge.
Courtesy Chicago Historical Society

7. Alone on the high plains, mountain men became adept at hunting-knife surgery. *Denver Public Library Western Collection*

8. Frontier army units in the Far West used horse-drawn ambulances when they could. *Historical Pictures Service–Chicago*

9. During the Indian wars wounded and sick soldiers were transported on travois when the terrain was too rough for ambulance wagons. *Courtesy Chicago Historical Society*

10. Thousands of forty-niners went to California by sea and the Isthmus of Panama, where they were often felled by fever and incarcerated in the hospital at Granada. *Courtesy Chicago Historical Society*

11. Dr. Drake found that Mississippi River steamers were crowded. Passengers packed into the lavatory to wash in the morning. *Courtesy Chicago Historical Society*

12. Among Chinese miners and railroad construction gangs barbers were often doctors as well. *Courtesy Chicago Historical Society*

13. Quack doctors toured the frontier dispensing cure-alls. *Historical Pictures Service–Chicago*

day and torches by night. In 1858 he took a seven-months leave to demonstrate his signals at Fort Hamilton, New York, and Old Point Comfort, Virginia.

"Oh, the telegraph will do," one officer said as he watched soldiers wigwagging with flags. "We can't bother with these balloons and whirligig flags and colored lamps and Fourth of July fireworks."

Dr. Myer became the chief signal officer of the U. S. Army, set up the Signal Corps, and extended military telegraph lines throughout the West to help troopers fight the Indians. For decades on the frontier military doctors had studied the weather. Dr. Myer made the task official. In 1870 he persuaded Congress to pass legislation which stated, "That the Secretary of War be and is hereby authorized and required to provide for taking meteorological observations at the military stations in the interior of the continent and at other points in the states and territories of the United States, and for giving notice on the northern lakes and on the sea coast by magnetic telegraph and marine signals of the approach and force of storms."

The U. S. Weather Bureau began its service to the public under the direction of Chief Signal Officer Myer. Throughout the West military doctors made their observations and sent the information over Dr. Myer's new telegraph lines. In 1871 doctors spotted a huge cold wave edging across the wilderness toward Texas, and for the first time farmers were issued an accurate weather prediction and were able to prepare for the storm.

The doctor was many things in a fort besides physician, surgeon, scientist, and weatherman. Sometimes he was the commander. Dr. William Cameron McKay, whose mother was a Chinook and whose father was part Indian, commanded two companies of friendly Indians in General Cook's campaign against the Snakes and Piutes. Captain John Summers, a surgeon, also was the commanding officer of Fort Kearny, Nebraska, in 1861. A doctor was also the counselor and chaplain, mapmaker, and veterinarian. When the garrison cat became sick with membraneous croup, Dr. Kober put the pet in an officer's cavalry boot and administered a touch of chloroform. The cat got well. Throughout the frontier military surgeons were expected to guard the health of horses and mules.

Sometimes a doctor negotiated with the Indians. Chief Surgeon J. S. Weiser of the 1st Minnesota Mounted Rangers, rode with the troops into the Dakotas, where they met a formidable band of Sioux. The doctor, recognizing some of the Indian chiefs whom he had once treated, offered to palaver with them in the hope of preventing bloodshed. He rode forth to a parley held three hundred yards from the army camp. As he talked with the chiefs, a fractious brave shot him dead, and the bitter Battle of the Mound began.

Dr. McGillycuddy also played a dramatic roll in an encounter between soldiers and Indians. In May 1877, Crazy Horse, victor over both Custer and Crook, sent for the doctor to treat his ailing wife. The doctor took care of the sick woman, and Crazy Horse became his friend. A few years and many battles later, the great war chief came to Fort Robinson in western Nebraska to make peace.

Dr. McGillycuddy watched as vengeful soldiers scuffled with the chief and stabbed him with a bayonet. Pushing his way through the jeering men, the doctor saw Crazy Horse writhing on the ground, blood pouring from his right hip, froth from his mouth. The chief's rapidly dropping pulse told the doctor that his death was near. When a captain demanded that the dying man be taken to the guardhouse, the doctor refused. He insisted that a prison was not the right place for a chief to die. Instead he carried him into the adjutant's office. There with Touch the Cloud, the chief's aged great-uncle, looking on, he gave Crazy Horse a morphine shot to ease his pain.

The light from a kerosene lamp shone on the chief's fevered face. He awoke and, looking up at the doctor, said, "*How kola,*" a last expression of his friendship. The doctor gave him another hypo. The chief's breath rasped. Outside a bugle sounded taps. The chief roused himself at the hated military call, looked about him, and died. The doctor gave the Indian sign of death to the old uncle.

Touch the Cloud drew a blanket over the body of Crazy Horse.

"That is the lodge of Crazy Horse," he said. Then he pointed upward. "The chief has gone above."

That night old Touch the Cloud slept before the door of Dr. McGillycuddy, guarding the man who afterward was known among the Indians as Crazy Horse's friend. Soon the Indian wars were to end, and the military doctor, who even in war remembered his humanity, would give way to doctors in civilian garb.

Chapter IX

RIVER-BOAT DOCTORS

A Missouri River doctor once claimed he had "dispensed enough calomel to load a paddle steamer and cupped enough blood to float it."

Another doctor eschewed calomel as treatment for his river-boat patients. Why use calomel when the muddy water of the river itself was a far more effective purgative? Both doctors might have disagreed with a river-boat captain who claimed that Mississippi River water was as nourishing as it was soupy with mud.

"A glass of river water is a meal in itself," he told passengers who wondered at seeing him scoop up a drink from the passing current.

Nathaniel Fisk Moore, a traveler on an Ohio River steamer in 1845, found no reason for faith in river water. He drank a cup of the silt-laden liquid and soon fell ill with violent intestinal cramps. For several days he dosed himself with elixir of opium. Then, as he wrote in his diary, he "took upon my own prescription 12 grains of calomel and 15 of jalap." This double-barreled dose did him no apparent good, and when the steamer paddled up to the dock at Cumberland, he was in agony. He struggled to the home of the only doctor in town, took one look at the tumble-down dwelling, and turned away, preferring to go on suffering than to entrust himself to a man who could live in such a place.

If passenger Moore looked with fear and suspicion on this Cumberland representative of the medical profession in western river towns, the medical profession had grave doubts about river-boat passengers. The physician-editor of the infant *Iowa Medical Journal* wrote in 1855 at Keokuk:

"Scarcely a boat from the south landed at our port during the last season from early spring until late in the fall on board which there was not one or more sick persons, and oftimes a corpse, requiring the rites of sepulture."

He pronounced Mississippi River steamboats to be floating pest-houses with obnoxious water in their bilges. The boats reeked from bow to stern with the stench of their unwashed human and animal cargo. He described dinner in the "dining quarters":

"The air of this limited and crowded apartment is filled with a compound aroma made up of food in process of cooking, odors of carbonizing oils, the foul emanations from the fecal evacuations of children, the stench from the excrement of cattle or horses which often flank decks on each side, the exhalations from decaying straw and decomposing grain, some of which has been littered and strewed over a humid deck floor, constitute no exaggerated picture of the conditions of very many of the steamers which have arrived at our port during the past year."

With one flourish of his editorial pen the doctor sweeps away the delightful visions of a century later—visions of nineteenth-century passengers cruising up the river, sipping mint juleps beneath gently whooshing fans, supping on gourmet cuisine on their way to adventure along the upper waters where buffalo only waited to be shot and Indians readily responded to the gun's imperious invitation to "bite the dust." Instead we see travelers reposing on filthy mattresses in staterooms too small for ventilation, where the upper berth is preferred even though lying in it the traveler must, says the editor, breathe "the foul expired air of the humble and lowly just under him."

If the traveler ventures into the salon, Nathaniel Fisk Moore assures us, he will find it, "crowded with card tables and a rowdy swaggering set who are playing, drinking, swearing and spitting in eager competition with each other." If a careless stream of tobacco juice misses a spittoon and sprays his shoes, the traveler is wise either not to take offense or to back up his complaint with a Bowie knife or a pistol. Probably the heat from the sun beating on the deck overhead and from the boilers will soon drive him to the bow in any case.

Timothy Flint, a missionary who traveled widely on western rivers during the early part of the nineteenth century, recollected that river emigrants generally suffered some kind of sickness. They talked about their bouts with harrowing afflictions as "seasoning" and took it as a matter of course. Flint described such a bout:

"First day I was prostrated to infantine weakness, and felt with its first attack that it was a thing very different from what I had yet experienced. Paroxysms of derangements occurred the third day. I continually supposed that I heard two flutes playing harmonies in the exquisite and delightful airs."

His treatment was a "painful process of blistering and emetics," which did him little good. Visitors to his cabin appeared to levitate and wore halos of light about their heads. The illness ran its course in a few months, and he could consider himself seasoned.

During the winter deck crews on western steamers suffered from frostbite and lung infections because there was no place to shelter from the cold, the wind, and the rain. Passengers escaped outdoor hardships, but packed into cramped quarters as they were, they became easy marks for contagious disease. Crew and passengers might well celebrate when the bitter northern weather brought navigation to a complete halt on the upper rivers. Then on the Mississippi at least the colorful ice express took to the frozen surface. Horses pulled huge sleighs filled with roistering travelers from port to port. Bells jingled merrily, and passengers, warm beneath fur robes, sang and nipped from hip flasks. Winter's cold lost its sting when at night everybody crowded around huge bonfires built on the river bank. An occasional roasted shin was the only likely casualty of a winter's night beneath the frosty stars.

Moreover, there were no mosquitoes in the winter. River boats that tied up at a bank for a summer's night or stopped to take on fuel at one of the woodyards on the shore were overwhelmed by clouds of minuscule vampires. No doctor on the river related the ague to the insects, but all agreed it was particularly rampant below St. Louis.

Traveler Timothy Flint wrote of the Mississippi between St. Louis and New Madrid that "diseases of the lungs are less frequent than at the North. The general type of the disorders is bilious. When the fevers are continued, they are terrible, and too often fatal. But most of the fevers are either remittents or intermittents, and when skilfully managed are seldom mortal. They are easily managed, but are apt to return. Their frequent returns and the course of medicine necessary to check them, soon break down the constitution. Rheumatism and dropsical affectations are common in the country. The two grand remedies, and what almost completes the list of medicines used here, are bark and calomel."

Flint spoke from experience; in one year he suffered seventy attacks of ague. He also suffered from influenza. Finally after ten years in the settlements, his health was so undermined that he returned to his native New England to nurse his ills and write his memoirs, a classic account of what life was like when steamboats were whistling around the bends of western rivers.

Timothy Flint survived an awesome array of western diseases, but he did not meet Vibrio comma, the king killer of the rivers. Long endemic in India, Vibrio comma, Asiatic cholera, spread to all parts of the world in the 1830s and 1840s. It followed caravan routes with the plodding feet of camels, accompanied the faithful on holy pilgrimages through desert wastes, crossed the oceans with ships of the line and ships of commerce, and fell upon defenseless Europe and the Americas. Some doctors believe German emigrants brought the deadly epidemic to the eastern United States in the 1840s, but there were earlier cases at New Orleans where Vibrio comma, still intent upon following transportation routes, boarded steamers to voyage upstream to the frontier.

Cholera struck with suddenness. On May 6, 1835, the English writer Harriet Martineau boarded the Mississippi River steamer, *Henry Clay*. River men and backwoodsmen clambered aboard. Some, who were working their passage by loading wood at the fuel stops along the way, stretched out on the deck. Just before the boat cast off, a last deck passenger hurried aboard. He flung down his pack among the others and went to sleep.

That night the last arrival awoke with terrifying muscular cramps and vomiting. His deck neighbors, aroused by his groans, called a New York doctor who was making the trip. Before the doctor reached the man, he was dead. Early in the morning, while most passengers were still sleeping, the body was buried at a "wooding up" place on the river bank. At the captain's request, Harriet Martineau and other witnesses kept the incident quiet so that the passengers would not panic.

This was the only death that Miss Martineau recorded on her trip, which was odd, for cholera usually spread quickly. The disease traveled up the rivers with the paddle boats that "walked upon the waters." It killed in ones and twos, killed in dozens, scores, hundreds; and then in St. Louis there were 4500 deaths. Men in excellent health felt uneasy in the stomach. There was a burning in the intestines, a craving for cold drinks, vomiting, then intestinal spasms and a pitiful weakness. The circulation slowed, the eyes sank, and the skin became cold. Death took at least half of the persons cholera infected.

"The disease is spread though baleful air," said doctors, and they argued learnedly about swamp odors and noxious exhalations from cities, about the need to plant trees in cities or to cut trees in cities. The steamboat *Yellowstone*, Captain Bennett in command, left St. Louis for the upper Missouri. Cholera sailed with the ship. So many of the crew were dead before the boat reached the mouth of the Kansas River, the site of modern Kansas City, that the captain went ashore to return to St. Louis for more men. He left William Labarge in charge of the *Yellowstone*.

The captain had no sooner started for St. Louis than the frightened settlers on the Missouri bank gave Labarge an ultimatum: leave or we'll burn the ship to the water. There was no choice for Labarge but to fire the boilers by himself and pilot and captain the ship with its dying crew to a point above the mouth of the Kansas River, outside of Missouri. The dead were secretly buried ashore. This was Labarge's first encounter with cholera. Later, when he became one of the most famous of the Missouri River captains, cholera was a familiar adversary.

"There is one spot just below Kansas City," he said in his old age, "I could point it out now, where I buried eight cholera victims in one grave. I could easily name a hundred localities along the river where I have buried passengers or crew. . . . It will never be known how many of these forgotten graves there are, but enough to make the banks of the Missouri River one continuous cemetery from its source to its mouth."

The steamboat *St. Ange*, sailing for the American Fur Company, left St. Louis for Fort Union in Montana. There were on board a hundred trappers and traders, two Jesuit missionaries, Fathers Hoecken and DeSmet, and Dr. Evans, a physician making a scientific journey for the Smithsonian Institution. Five hundred miles upriver cholera broke out. The Jesuits and the doctor fought Vibrio comma with no success. They could only make death less terrifying. Twelve days out of St. Louis, Father Hoecken died.

Dr. W. W. Mayo, father of the celebrated Mayo brothers who founded the clinic at Rochester, Minnesota, first met cholera on a river steamer taking him to the Minnesota frontier. In 1854 he knew of no effective treatment for cholera, and he could only give the dying men such remedies as Perry Davis Pain Killer and spoonsful of red pepper mixed in whiskey. Both cures were often resorted to by crewmen and passengers. Dr. Mayo's patients died. Their bodies were covered with canvas until nightfall, when they were buried in rough coffins on islands or where the boat stopped to take on wood.

It was Dr. John Evans who first realized how cholera was spread. When a young doctor in the Indian backwoods, he was accustomed to sleeping on hard puncheon floors beneath his well-worn buffalo robe as he rode on his rounds through the settlements. He collected his fees in corn and potatoes and could not find any cash to replenish his store of medicine. A neighboring doctor, Isaac Fisher, was in the same plight, so the two physicians loaded a flatboat with their produce and drifted down the Wabash, the Ohio, and the Mississippi to New Orleans.

John Evans was cut of the same cloth as his teacher, Daniel Drake, and as he went, he studied the conditions of life and commerce along the rivers. This doctor, who was to become the founder of both Northwestern University and the University of

Denver, a builder of western railroads and the first territorial governor of Colorado, returned north with a firm understanding of the role of transportation in the winning of the West.

Dr. Evans observed also the way in which river steamers spread disease from port to port so that it reached the most remote towns. When cholera appeared at New Orleans, Dr. Evans traced its progress up the Mississippi and its tributaries. He tabulated cases showing how its victims had invariably been in touch with a contaminated person or thing. Armed with his studies, he boldly attacked the theory held by most doctors that currents of foul air carried cholera mysteriously across the land and the sea.

"To explain the spread of cholera by the atmospheric theory requires us to suppose in the first place that the air is contaminated," he argued. "Then that this poisoned air travels regardless of the course of the winds . . . That small bodies of it may go to great distances in very narrow channels . . . That a streak of it crosses the ocean . . . at a single point, and invariably that point a sea-port town. Then that it will tarry a month at the quarantine within eight miles of New York City . . . Then that it will travel the whole length of the navigable waters of the Mississippi and its tributaries without varying to the right or left, and that it will hover over ships, steamboats and caravans as they journey on their way."

Dr. Evans demanded that Congress enact a national quarantine law to halt all trade which spread cholera. The western doctor was ahead of his day, and not only congressmen but his fellow physicians were unimpressed. Cholera was allowed to come ashore from river steamers at ports in the wilderness and to march unchecked over the western trails.

Deadly as it may have been, cholera probably was not the leading cause of death on western rivers. The *Iowa Medical Journal* of 1855 pointed out the dangers of "collisions, explosions, burnings and snaggings." Snaggings and collisions sank more boats, but explosions and fires took more lives. Sixty miles below Memphis there was an explosion aboard the *Pennsylvania* as the boat passed Ship Island. Mark Twain's brother Henry was aboard.

At 6 A.M. on that summer morning the boat was steaming placidly up the river when pilot George Ealer rang for full steam. Twain wrote in *Life on the Mississippi*, "The next moment four of the eight boilers exploded with a thunderous crash, and the whole forward third of the boat was hoisted toward the sky! The main part of the mass, with the chimneys, dropped upon the boat again, a mountain of riddled and chaotic rubbish—and then, after a little while, fire broke out."

Many of the cabin passengers and the three to four hundred deck riders were flung into the river and drowned. Others breathed scalding steam into their lungs and died. Fire burned some; flying debris maimed others. A crowbar was driven through a man's body. As usually happened in a river disaster, the survivors were taken to the nearest port, in this case Memphis, where Henry Clemens was seen by a doctor.

Mark Twain wrote, "The physicians examined his injuries and saw that they were fatal, and naturally turned their main attention to patients who could be saved."

Forty wounded men were placed upon pallets on the floor of a public hall. Memphis women came daily with flowers, fruits, and delicacies and nursed the wounded. Doctors and medical students stood on watch against death. Twain arrived in Memphis on another boat and went to the makeshift hospital.

"I entered that large hall—two long rows of prostrate forms—more than 40 in all," he wrote, "and every face and head a shapeless wad of loose raw cotton . . . I watched there six days and nights . . . There was one daily incident which was peculiarly depressing; this was the removal of the doomed to a chamber apart. It was done in order that the morale of the other patients might not be injuriously affected by seeing one of their number in the death agony. The fated one was always carried out with as little stir as possible, and the stretcher was always hidden from sight by a wall of assistants; but no matter: everybody knew what that cluster of bent forms, with its muffled step and its slow movement, meant; and all eyes watched it wistfully, and a shudder went abreast of it like a wave."

The chief mate was carried to the death room more than once. His scalded body was swathed in linseed oil and raw cotton to the waist. Doctors tried to allay his pain with morphine, but he would not take it because he claimed his wife had been killed by the treacherous drug. On the evening of the sixth day, Henry Clemens was carried to the death room, and he did not return. One hundred and fifty passengers died in the *Pennsylvania* explosion and fire, a tragedy notable among hundreds of similar disasters only in that it killed the brother of a talented author who made it representative of the danger that rode paddle-wheel boats when steam was in its infancy and western rivers were hazardous with snags and shifting bars and banks. This was a day when a doctor on the river often found that there was little for him to do but make dying a more comfortable procedure.

Chapter X

PHYSICIANS OF THE WAGON TRAINS

When Andrew Broadus, a driver, saw the wolf skulking along the hill crest in the August heat, he grabbed his gun by the muzzle and pulled it from the tail of his wagon. Somehow the trigger caught; the gun roared, and the ball shattered the bones of his forearm. At the gunshot the wagon train toiling westward over the Santa Fe Trail halted. The wagon master galloped back along the line to Broadus' wagon. He took one look at the bloody arm.

"It'll have to come off," he said.

"No," said Broadus, and he would not let the wagon master amputate, even though he knew as well as the next man that the mangled flesh would soon start to putrefy in the heat. The wagons rattled on westward. Spots crept up higher on Broadus' arm. Terrified by the close approach of death, he gave in. He lay on the buffalo grass one evening and begged that somebody, anybody take a knife and cut. The men soothed him, but none could steel himself to try his hand at surgery. Then a skinny sixteen-year-old boy spoke up.

"I kin do it," he said.

"Y're too young, Kit. Let somebody else do it," said a hunter. Young Kit Carson had run away from home and was on his first trip west. Later he would go into the mountains to become one of the greatest fur trappers and frontier scouts. The hunter had carved many a buffalo hump, and now heartened by the boy's pluck, he prepared with the help of two volunteers to carve human flesh. He whetted his skinning knife. A teamster got out a rusty handsaw from his tool box, but the hunter allowed that the teeth were too coarse. The teamster set to work filing a fine set of teeth on the back of the saw. Other men built a small but hot fire, and a king bolt removed from one of the wagons was placed on it.

The volunteer surgeons put the patient on his back on the grass and tied a rope around his arm as a tourniquet. A dozen men held him fast. Kneeling at his side, the hunter opened the arm all around the bone. He took the saw and in an instant cut through the bone. He seared the raw stump with the white-hot bolt to seal the arteries. Then he rubbed cool axle grease over the wound and bandaged it. Broadus lay in the shade of the wagon through the day. He slept well that night, and in the morning the wagon train moved on as if nothing had happened. The stump began to heal at once, and in a few weeks Broadus was active and well.

Only a few wagon trains were lucky enough to have a doctor along. Men and women placed their faith in their own skill and the medical books and emergency kits they had with them. Dr. C. M. Clark, who accompanied a wagon train in 1860 in the Pikes Peak gold rush, observed: "Every man had a package of drugs and nostrums, with written directions for use, sometimes consisting of blue pills, a little ipecac and opium, together with a bottle of peppermint, pain killer and somebody's 'sovereign remedy for all ills.'"

Dr. Clark testily advised pioneers to leave their medicines at home and "pay more attention to the quality and quantity of food used, and be more careful in the matter of exposure."

Sometimes a wagon master became noted for his medical acumen, and families would join his train to be safeguarded from the diseases that infested the trails. Sol Tetherow was such a wagon master on the Oregon Trail. He relied heavily on wild ginger tea to effect his cures. How much should a patient take?

"Always git all you can but youse what you can git," he said. Some of Tetherow's medical recipes still survive. He mixed this cough syrup to relieve the croup in children traveling with his train:

"Boil the lickrish root to thick molasses. Take 1 fluid ounce, ½ ounce Balm Gilaid buds, 1 gil. vinigar, 1 gil. strong surup of skunk cabbage root, ½ fluid ounce tincter labelea. Take a tea spoon full or so often as the case requires to keep the phlegm loos to rais easy."

When wagon master Tetherow spooned this mixture into a child who was troubling the night with a racking cough, the small patient soon dozed off, and the wagon train could get some sleep.

Sometimes the afflictions of the trail were cured by a stray mountain man, hunter, or Indian medicine man. Sometimes a granny or midwife was along. One Oregon-bound wagon train was fortunate to include Elizabeth Perry, a seventeen-year-old bride from Iowa, who showed a talent for healing. Although she had never received medical training, she delivered babies on the journey and lost only one mother and child. She scoured the country for herbs and tended the sick. When she reached Oregon, she raised a family of her own and hung out a sign at her homestead which read: MRS. E. PERRY, DOCTRESS.

Typhoid fever, scurvy, smallpox, cholera, tuberculosis, and wounds inflicted by the Indians all took their toll. "Sickness often visited the emigrant," wrote Dr. Clark in Colorado. "The prevailing diseases were bilious fever, which often assumed a typhoid character, pleurisy, pneumonia and scurvy, and besides there were many other incidental ailments which were excited into action by exposure, insufficient and improper food and overexertion. Many were suffering from rheumatism, ophthalmia. I mentioned scurvy as one of the prevailing diseases but do not remember having seen a pure case; it was often, however, a complication, and I neglected to state that diarrhoea and dysentery were prevalent."

The sick were carried in the wagon resting atop the load. Exposed to weather and the jolting action, they usually got sicker instead of better. Nostalgia, according to Dr. Clark, also "exercised a most baneful influence, seemingly paralyzing all life and hope, filling the mind with corroding fears and frustrating every vital energy."

J. Goldsborough Bruff in his *Gold Rush Journals* describes a pioneer family on the trail in the Far West. An old man, sick with flux and scurvy, rode a horse. Beneath him was a mattress to cushion his aching bones from the jaded mount's gait. Around him was a coverlet. Pale and haggard, he stayed on the horse by holding to its neck. Another man sick with fever and ague plodded by on a mule. Women in the wagons chocked the wheels on the hills, and ten-year-old boys led the animals.

With each party of pioneers running a wilderness gauntlet of disease, accidents and wounds, a wagon train which had a doctor along was expected to share him with all others in the vicinity. Dr. John Powell on the Oregon Trail in 1852 not only cared for the sick of his own train, but rode fifty miles to care for patients with other trains. He delivered babies and fought typhoid and cholera, which he came to believe were spread by contaminated drinking water. He advised pioneers to stay away from the water holes and organized teams of well diggers to go ahead and dig clean wells. He insisted that wagon trains keep the wells clean for pioneers still to come.

Cholera was the most fearful of the deaths that stalked the western trails. On the Overland Trail to the California gold fields 200 emigrants had already died of cholera as early as June 7, 1849, east of Fort Kearney, Nebraska, alone. By 1850 there were 40 cholera graves along the 60 miles of trail through Plum Creek Valley. Between the Missouri River and Fort Laramie there were 700 graves, the final resting places of the poor wretches who drank from the stagnant pools and water holes instead of from the Platte River. Dr. William R. Allen, who traveled overland to Oregon in 1850, reported that from 2000–3000 emigrants died of cholera on the Oregon Trail that year. He himself cared for 700 cases and claimed good success when treatment was begun early enough.

As J. Goldsborough Bruff pushed westward with a wagon train in 1849, he observed frequent graves of cholera victims. Then on July 8 cholera struck his own train. A man was stricken as they were hitching up the mules one morning. Bruff says he "drank of slew water." Mad with agony, he begged his friends to shoot him. The next day he was dead, and Bruff set down a spare poetic version of a trail death.

The surgeon's skill—
and his messmate's will—
Were exerted, alas! in vain—
For the hour of noon,
Came sorrowing, Soon,
When the faded corse was lain!
With mournful look—
For a shroud they took—
His blanket—and sew'd him round;—
and that banner bright—
once his soul's delight—
o'er his breathless form was bound!

Since fear of contagion kept even the Indians from robbing cholera graves, some wily travelers dug false graves and cached provisions or valuables in them. They erected crosses bearing their own name and the frightening legend, DIED OF CHOLERA. A St. Louis doctor on his way to the settlement on Great Salt Lake dug such a grave and hid five hundred dollars' worth of medicine in it. Later he sent a wagon out from Salt Lake to bring in his hoard. To his dismay someone had broken in and removed two hundred dollars' worth of drugs. The thief left a note giving his regrets and correctly estimating the worth of the medicine he took. He very likely was another doctor.

Cholera frightened pioneers even before they set out on the trail. Any digestive upset was imagined to be the dread killer. Army doctor William Hammond, Jr., stationed at Fort Kearney, Nebraska, in June 1850 observed that California emigrants suffered a great deal from a disease which they called cholera. Actually it was acute diarrhea brought about by poor diet and the hardships of traveling across the high plains. He reported with disapproval the emigrants' nostrum of brandy and cayenne pepper and treated the sufferers with calomel and opium stringents.

A wagon-train doctor sometimes was also captain of the train. Dr. Elijah White led a train of 100 settlers to Oregon in 1842.

Dr. Justin Millard led a party to the northwest from Keokuk, Iowa, in 1852. Hardships, exposure, and cholera destroyed Dr. Millard's health. He gave all the funds he had to the needy en route and arrived in Portland penniless and sick. Other doctors were more fortunate. In 1853 Dr. Thomas Flint of Maine, incredibly enough, drove 2000 sheep and a few oxen, horses and cows from Illinois to California through hostile Indians. He stood off the attacks of bear and wolves and brought his livestock across the Mohave Desert and through Cajon Pass. He settled down to practice at San Juan Bautista. That same year Dr. Jesse Scott Cunningham and a party brought a still greater herd of 4000 sheep overland from the Midwest. En route 375 sheep died. Dr. Cunningham paid seventy-five cents a head for them and sold them for eleven dollars a head in Sacramento.

Doctors who took the trails west did so for reasons as varied as were those of other pioneers. They looked for an adventurous release from humdrum practices in the East; they traveled west for their health; they sought gold or land; they wished to save lives. In 1852 Dr. Anson Henry, who had cared for Abraham Lincoln when he suffered his emotional disturbance, treated cholera on the western trails. When the Stephen Meek party was lost in the mountains of central Oregon in 1845 while seeking a short cut to the Willamette River, Dr. Ralph Wilcox was with them. He tended the dying as the food and water ran out. Cheerful and rotund Dr. Theophilus Degen, known to his wagon train as the "Dutch doctor," looked out for the Sager children after their father died in Wyoming, and brought them safely over the Oregon Trail to Dr. Whitman's mission on the Walla Walla.

Forty-two-year-old Dr. David Maynard was a fugitive from a sharp-tongued wife and $30,000 in debts back home in Ohio. When he joined a westering wagon train his sole possessions were his mule, a buffalo robe, a gun, a few books, and his surgical instruments. Dr. Maynard tended cholera cases until he contracted cholera himself. He recovered because, as he observed in his diary, nobody meddled with him. Ninety miles west of Fort Kearney he stopped one afternoon to care for an emigrant family which was down with the cholera. Before morning the husband, son, and mother of comely Mrs. Israel Brashears were dead. The doctor put his scanty belongings into the tearful widow's wagon, and they started down the trail. When they reached the west coast, the doctor married the widow.

Between one winter and the next, emigrants to California and Oregon had to cover 2000 miles. The mountains were high; the deserts were wide. Pioneers traveled in a wooden box on wheels, nine to ten feet long and four feet wide with a canvas top supported by bent hickory bows. Wagon tongues and front axles snapped but could sometimes be replaced. Wheels broke, and the wagon had to be abandoned. Heat, dust, and mosquitoes plagued the emigrants. Always the wagon trains raced against the winter's first snowfall in the high mountain passes. Isaac Jones Wistar, later to be a Union general in the Civil War, traveled west with a wagon train and kept a diary which offers laconic testimony to the inexorable nature of the contest with the advancing season. Sickness could not be allowed to stay the wagons.

"May 8th. Waiting in camp on J.'s illness. If it should be small pox, we will be in a bad way, as we could neither carry him on nor expect Lipscombe to keep him in his one-roomed log cabin. To empty a wagon and haul him back to Independence would cause delay that might have serious results, in case we should arrive at the Sierra too late to cross this year."

The wagon train pressed on when J. was slightly improved. J. grew worse again. At the insistence of the train doctor the pioneers paused again so that J. could die in peace. Then they were off again on their journey that must lead over the mountains before winter.

In the evening by the trailside the life of the pioneering families went on. Children played and were disciplined. Women cooked the meals while men watered the stock and repaired the wagons. There was time in the evening for love and friendship, talk, the strumming of a banjo, and the songs of home. The campfires glowed within the circle of wagons. After a hard day's march a doctor still had to go from wagon to wagon to take care of his patients. He dispensed such medicines as Dover's powder, dragon's blood, Peruvian bark, and calomel. He bled, cupped, and leeched. He used carbolic acid for antisepsis and employed knife and saw to amputate and probe. He set broken bones and patched up heads of brawling men. He carried a small supply of candy to cure the evening misery of a homesick child. When all but the guards bedded down, he too crawled into his blankets and was thankful for the rest at the end of the day.

Chapter XI

SURGEONS AROUND THE HORN

The British bark *John Ritson* was becalmed off the coast of Lower California. The tropical sun burnished the impassive sea. Lassitude and death spread among the emigrants bound for the gold fields. As he prepared to drop the body of a deceased passenger into the deep, the American ship's surgeon, James Tyson, studied the faces of the living. To him it seemed, "The complexion of every man was that of an extremely sallow hue, approaching more to the lividness of death than anything I can describe."

The doctor released the body for its final dismal plunge and returned to the sick bay where the still living urgently required his attention. A slight breeze came up, and the ship moved slowly forward. To sail the ship through such a sea was like "flogging a toad through tar," thought the doctor. His sick suffered from Panama fever, which, not knowing anything about yellow fever he attributed to eating tropical fruits and drinking too much claret and ale. He changed the dressings on a leg wound which one passenger had inflicted on himself with his dirk while helping to push the shore boat away from the dock at Taboga.

In an effort to stay disease, the doctor from time to time cleansed and fumigated the hold and required passengers and crew to take daily baths in sea water. One night at 2 A.M. he was roused from his sleep to revive a man who had pitched head first through the hatchway into the hold. Considering the stifling heat, the poorly ventilated cabins, the miserable rations served perversely by the British crew as breakfast at noon and tea at 7 P.M., it did not surprise the doctor that he had so many patients. As he fed body after body to the fishes, he observed philosophically that the victims were only paying nature's debt.

Dr. Tyson had taken one of the four sea routes to the California gold fields, confident that he had chosen the healthy way to travel to the Golden West. These routes were largely favored by inhabitants of the eastern seaboard and the Gulf Coast. Let the backwoodsmen west of the Alleghenies trek across the continent in covered wagons while Indians took potshots at them. Coast people responded instead to the advertisements and brochures of the shipping companies, which offered an easy sea voyage around Cape Horn or to Panama, Nicaragua, and Mexico, where emigrants were told they could junket overland through a paradise of flowers to a west coast port and catch the first steamer or sailboat heading north.

It did not take Dr. Tyson long to learn that the advertising was more eloquent than accurate. Crossing the Gulf of Mexico the heat was so intense that the captain's ale barrel blew up and drenched the passengers. Dr. Tyson landed at Chagres to find fever on every hand, a fever which he did not understand and could not cure. He set off across the Isthmus, paddling up the Chagres River in canoes with other Gold Rush Americans. At night they built bonfires on shore to keep off wild beasts, snakes, and insects. Dr. Tyson counted six alligators to the average mile and observed an enormous tiger cat lapping from the stream as they paddled past. Panama was a kaleidoscope of fevers, of nearly nude damsels, bad coffee, the barking of dogs, squealing of pigs, ringing of cracked bells in village churches, of torrential rains, of flea-bitten nights and days so hot that the doctor was certain eggs could be boiled in the shade. He completed his trip by mule and on the Pacific Coast signed on the *John Ritson* as ship's surgeon in exchange for his passage to San Francisco. Later he wrote down his advice to Americans traveling to California over the Isthmus route.

"Engage a canoe," he told his readers, "and keep the natives at their work as long as you can, without over fatigue at one time. This is indispensable, or you may be kept on the river longer than is necessary or desirable."

He urged that travelers carry as little baggage as possible, no package to weigh more than fifty pounds, and provisions for three to four days. Because the water was charged with decayed vegetable matter, he suggested that nobody should drink it unless it was at least mixed with ale, claret, or port wine. Brandy was to be avoided and so was the heat of the sun and the night air.

The other routes across the waist of the Americas were no healthier, and thousands of Gold Rush passengers chose to take the 15,000-mile, nine-month voyage around Cape Horn. That first year of 1849 over five hundred ships made this trip. Some were the pride of the American merchant marine; others were leaky craft that only stayed afloat through the exertions of crew and passengers at the pumps. According to Dr. G. R. B. Horner, noted ship's surgeon of the day, even the finer ships left much to be asked. He observed that ship owners built "merchant ships for beauty and holding large cargoes." Cabins were small and "pure air unknown in them."

Dr. Horner was appalled by the accommodations he saw aboard steamers sailing from the east coast to California. Forward passengers were crowded in berths in the bows or about the forecastle. Two or three individuals slept in a berth which was invariably "so short that no man of good height could be in them at full length." Tiers of narrow bunks were erected below the main deck of many ships. In good weather the passengers remained on deck and breathed the air, but when storms lashed the seas they had to stay below in their shelflike bunks, holding on for dear life to the sides so that they would not be pitched out on the deck. Since passengers and crew rarely changed clothes or bathed, a man's own offensive odor was his only defense against the odor of his companions. Crowded below deck, passengers were easy prey to colds and pulmonary complaints. Rheumatism and chilblains awaited those who kept to the deck in blustery weather.

Despite the hardships and hazards of the deck, some passengers, out of boredom, voluntarily helped the crew sail the ship. In heavy seas they climbed the rigging, reefed the sails, and hauled ropes. They were drenched for days on end. Because their quarters were so damp and cold, their clothing never dried out between watches. Sooner or later all but the hardiest became the doctor's patients.

Food on the *John Ritson*, said Dr. Tyson, was mainly of vegetable origin, but it contained animal life, minute and not too tasty to the squeamish. Most ships, according to Dr. Horner, were provisioned largely with bread and meat. Biscuits were made of wheat flour with rice sometimes added for variety. When the ships put into port, the cooks went ashore and bought fresh bread, some of which was tasty, but most of which was baked from maggoty flour. The bread was usually hard, but the bread bought in Bahia, Brazil, was the hardest of all.

"It was too hard for any ordinary teeth to chew," said Dr. Horner, "and required hammering to be got into fragments."

Rice was insipid in taste and so apt to constipate those who ate it that doctors made it into a gruel flavored with pleasant condiments to feed to passengers with loose bowels. Most of the meats were salted so highly that they had to be soaked for twenty-four hours in fresh water and washed before they could be eaten. Night after night passengers and crew dined on such high-seas cuisine as lobscouse, a hash of potatoes, salt beef or pork, and hard bread, and daddyfunk, a heavy pudding made of sea biscuit broken up and boiled in molasses.

Ships usually carried enough fresh or dried fruits to ward off scurvy. Many passengers also brought aboard their private stocks of fruit preserves, but during seven months of 1850 a Dr. Rogers, the port physician, inspected five hundred ships reaching San Francisco and found that half of them had cases of scurvy aboard. When he asked why the ships had not stopped en route to pick up fresh vegetables, the captains informed him that the owners had expressly forbidden such costly delays. The doctor, concerned with the plight of a young sailor whose teeth had grown so loose from scurvy that he spit out a couple at a time, was scandalized at the greed of the ship owners.

"Pork may be bad, the beef may be good," said Dr. Horner. "Should the bread be moldy and wormy, the rice may be sound;

if the cheese be spoiled, an additional quantity of butter can be allowed." But drinking water, concluded the doctor, has no substitutes. Doctors poured small amounts of quicklime, calcined lime, pure charcoal, and muriatic or sulphuric acid into barrels of water.

"It may not have any efficacy in preserving the water," commented Dr. Horner. "It certainly has some in preventing the decay of the casks."

Of all the water taken aboard during the long voyage around the Horn, doctors contended that the water of the La Plata River was the most tainted. Buenos Aires physicians urged that crews throw a little powdered alum into each cask to make it potable.

Despite or perhaps because of the agents added to the drinking water aboard ship, bowel infections were frequent and severe. Cholera, the dread killer of the overland trail, sailed with the ships too. The *Golden Gate* left from Panama City for San Francisco in August 1852, crowded with passengers and several companies of United States soldiers. Almost before the ship was beyond hailing distance from port, 84 were dead of cholera. In July 1855, the *Sierra Nevada* set sail from San Juan del Sur, Nicaragua, bound for California. Her captain saw 31 die of cholera before she reached San Francisco Bay ten days later. The *Uncle Sam* lost 104 out of 750 passengers to cholera, and 9 more died in San Francisco after the ship reached port. Doctors tried all kinds of remedies under the assumption that while there was life, there was hope, only to find that neither life nor hope lasted long once cholera set in. They tried to disinfect ships with fumes from burning sulphur, gunpowder, tar, tobacco, and vinegar, but cholera proved immune to the stench.

A doctor was almost as powerless against yellow fever. Frank Marryat, traveling to California with his wife, boarded a steamer at Panama in 1853. He was weak from a near fatal attack of yellow fever. His wife had no sooner boarded than she fell ill with the fever.

"There were two young doctors on board," wrote Marryat, "but both were attacked shortly after we started. Then the epidemic broke out among the passengers, who gave way to fear and could not be moved from the lower deck and so lay weltering in their own filth."

There was no medicine. To make matters worse the ship sprang a leak in a wild storm, and the able-bodied passengers had to join the crew in bailing to keep it afloat. The dead were dropped into the sea.

"From the scuttle-hole of our small cabin," said Marryat, "we could hear the splash of bodies as they were tossed overboard."

When the ship reached Acapulco, the Marryats went ashore, determined to seek passage to California on a less hapless vessel.

Smallpox was even more feared when it broke out at sea. The bark *Aquidneck* was at anchor in the harbor of Montevideo when a sailor fell ill. At first he complained of chills and fever, and he thought a dose of quinine would fix him up as good as new. Two days later, three more men came down with the same symptoms. The captain examined them.

"Rigid in the spine, and at the base of the brain," he said. "I knew by this that smallpox was among us!"

He ordered the distress signals hoisted. Thirty-six hours later a Uruguayan doctor rowed out to the ship and came aboard. He took a quick look at the sick men.

"Yes, your men have got smallpox," he said. "You must leave the port at once."

He jumped into his boat and rowed frantically away while the captain shouted imprecations at his lack of humanity. There was nothing to do but put out to sea. As he got the ship under way, the captain explained to the mate and the ship's carpenter how to mix medicines and disinfectants. The *Aquidneck* sailed for the Isle of Flores through gales, rain, and finally a hurricane. Reaching port at last the captain raised another distress signal. Once again a doctor rowed out, this time carrying a pound of sulphur, a pint of carbolic acid, and some barley. He, too, glanced at the sick sailors and fled the ship.

"What should I do with the men you are leaving to die?" the captain shouted after him.

The doctor pointed significantly to the water. That night the captain buried two dead men at sea. The *Aquidneck* sailed back to Montevideo, where this time the surviving sick were allowed ashore.

Often a ship took the long sea route to California without a doctor aboard. Boston, New York, and Philadelphia ships' druggists put out medical guides which were placed in the ship's medicine chest. Sometimes the cook or the mate, but more often the captain, studied these guides which ran the alphabet of diseases from apoplexy to yellow fever, and in an emergency tried to bring about cures. Dr. Henry W. Balch wrote *The Seaman's Medical Guide*, one of the best-known volumes, which was sold by Epes Sargent and Joseph H. Brown of Boston with their medical chest. The book not only described the diseases the captain-doctor might encounter at sea, but gave cures. It told him how to take a pulse and recommended that if one of his charges developed the delirium tremens, he should tie him to a bed and give him laudanum in quantity and every six hours a glass of his favorite liquor. To straighten out a mashed nose the captain should pass a piece of wire or a knitting needle into the nostrils and press the bones back into their proper position. If a woman started into labor, the captain was directed to tie a sheet to the foot of the bed for her to pull on. Armed with the book and the medicine chest, the captain was reckoned a match for ulcers and abscesses, whitlows and burns. In case he was timid at letting blood, Dr. Balch had this reassuring word:

"Every man should know how to bleed. It is an operation so extremely easy in itself, and so important in its effects, that it should be universally understood. There is no mystery, or difficulty in the matter, and any one who has command of his fingers and eyes, can acquire in five minutes that skill which may enable him to save the lives of many."

Dr. Balch might instead have addressed his reassurance to the patient, for many a sailor or passenger blanched when he saw the captain advancing upon him with his lancet nervously poised for action. At least Dr. Balch did not make the error of another doctor who prepared a book of medical instructions which were cleverly keyed to numbers on bottles in the ship's medicine chest. When one doctor-captain found he was all out of number nine, he blithely added numbers six and three together, confident that he would get the same happy result.

A page from the log of the *Courier* engaged in the California trade captures the perplexity and the tragedy of the doctor-captain confronted with a serious accident at sea with nothing but his book to guide him:

"Thursday 9th. March 1825

"All thru 24 hours strong gales from N West with rainy and squally weather.

"At 3:30 A M Leonard Wade fell from the Main Yard down upon the deck, from whence he was taken senseless into the cabin where every effort was made to recover him, such as bleeding, bathing in vinegar, etc., after which he was put to bed. He had convulsive fits about every 10 minutes in the intervals of which he appeared quite easy. We could not discover that any limbs were broken or any mark of injury, excepting a continual and copious flow of blood from his left ear.—

"At 8:30 A M he breathed his last.

"At 9 A M after prayers were read over him he was committed to the deep."

Doctors sailing around the Horn found that their medical practice took on a salt-water flavor. Sailors and passengers alike drank liquor to such excess that doctors learned to give vegetable bitters instead of wines or malt liquors so that their patients could not say, "doctor recommended them to drink spirits." In case of the DT's, a ship's surgeon might follow the cure suggested by Dr. Balch, or he might put the man's feet and legs in a tub of warm water and then apply mustard plasters to the feet and the nape of the neck.

More heroic cures were reserved for the common cold. Doctors brewed their own gargle of one teaspoon of pure African cayenne pepper, two teaspoons of common salt, two tablespoons of vinegar and half a pint of boiling water, all mixed well, cooled, and strained. This was calculated to knock out any sore throat. Boils were as common as the common cold because of shipboard diet. Doctors gave saline cathartics, magnesia, Epsom salts, and rhubarb and applied warm linseed poultices to bring the boil to a head. Then they lanced it, plucked out the core, and released plenty of blood to wash the wound clean. When there was no linseed oil handy, they made their poultices either from ship's biscuit steeped in boiling water and mingled with grease and oil, or from mashed potatoes. The same foods which caused the boils were in this way made to cure them.

The doctor's command post was the sick bay, which, Dr. Horner pointedly remarked, was crowded from amidships by a steamboat's machinery. There was no room abaft either, so the hapless sick were taken forward.

"This is the case even in the *San Jacinto*," he said, "one of our largest steam frigates, and more than 220 feet long. She indeed has no separate place for the sick; they have to lie near the fore hatch of the berth deck, and are exposed to both the heat of the galley or cooking range just abaft them and to the intense fires in the adjacent furnaces generating steam in the hold below."

In a storm, concluded the doctor, the sick had the "unhappy alternative of bearing its chilling blasts or of closing the hatches and being stewed in steam."

To protect his medical stores from moisture and from rats, mice, and vermin, the doctor kept everything in tin drawers and boxes. He locked up his supply of grog or it disappeared mysteriously, even though no mouse or rat would touch it.

From his fearsome lair, the doctor sallied forth to fight his war against measles and mumps, constipation, beriberi, and scurvy. For measles he gave cooling drinks and Seidlitz powders together with alum gargles if there were respiratory involvement. He attacked mumps with Epsom salts and tartar emetic and constipation with Epsom salts alone but in diabolic quantities. If a man was swept overboard and brought back on board in an unconscious condition, the doctor passed a curved tin tube through his nostrils. The tube was attached to a bellows with which the physician inflated his lungs. A much more modern technique required the doctor to place his mouth against that of the patient and blow air into his lungs. It was believed that if the doctor chewed garlic first this would have a more marked effect. If the man still did not revive, the doctor as a last resort might introduce tobacco smoke into his bowels.

Doctors who sailed the high-seas route to California shared the impressions of Latin American ports of call with the other argonauts. They marveled at women and children kneeling in prayer in the streets before ancient churches, the fierce battling of gamecocks, padres playing cards, meat cut in strips and sold by the yard, and calico sold by the pound. They hunted wild pigs on the Isle of Cocos on the Pacific side of Central America with the passengers, and one at least went in search of buried treasure. He was an Illinois doctor on his way around the Horn. In Costa Rica he succored a dying man, who told him of a hoard buried on the same Isle of Cocos where the wild pig gamboled. When he reached San Francisco, the doctor chartered the schooner *Julius Pringle* and sailed on his adventurous voyage. Landing on his own Treasure Island, he found everything as the dying man had described it, including the burial place, but somebody had already removed the treasure.

Doctors slept in the bamboo huts of the people at Chagres and waited for canoes in the blistering tropical heat and torrential rains. They were persecuted by mosquitoes, and they too fell ill. One stricken physician was determined to reach California, where he intended to build a hospital. Panamanians carried him across the Isthmus in a hammock and placed him on board a ship. There he died. He left all his money, a few hundred dollars, to the Governor of California and charged him with a piece of unfinished business. The money was left to endow the hospital which he had not lived to build himself.

Chapter XII

MEDICS OF THE MINING CAMPS

"I bet he dies," said a gambler.

He was watching Dr. Thomas D. Hodges examine Ezra Williams, who had been shot in a saloon brawl.

"Fifty dollars he don't," replied the doctor.

"Done!" exclaimed the gambler. "Anyone else want in this pot?"

The boys crowding the saloon in a California gold-mining camp in the 1850s quickly wagered a total of $14,600 in gold dust on Ezra's life. Dutch Kate swirled in and bet $10,000 that he would be dead by morning. Men who were optimistic about Ezra's chances covered her bet, as Dr. Holges placed Ezra on the pool table beneath a hanging lamp and bound up the wound.

Seated comfortably on chairs, bottles in hand, the miners watched Ezra wrestle with death. They cheered his groans or his bloody coughs, depending upon whether they had bet on life or death. At 2 A.M. Ezra was apparently dead, but the doctor succeeded in reviving him. At 4 A.M. he almost died again, only to have the doctor stave off death once more. At 5:50 A.M. Ezra finally expired. Dr. Hodges lost a patient and fifty dollars.

Dr. Hodges also lost medical prestige because a Gold Rush doctor was supposed to be good at pool-table surgery. Violence was routine in mining camps throughout the Old West. Miners who extracted $600,000,000 in gold from the California Mother Lode between 1849 and 1856 spent $6,000,000 on Bowie knives and pistols. During the first five years of the Gold Rush there were 4200 murders and 1400 suicides in California mining camps alone. In 1854 Downieville miners boasted that their town had grown uncommonly healthy in the first five months of 1854. There had been only two violent deaths and "one of these was a Chinaman."

A mining-camp doctor lived and practiced elbow to elbow with trouble. When young Dr. Charles Fox Gardiner arrived in western Colorado, he bunked at a hotel next to a saloon aptly called the Slaughter Pen. Returning home from one of his first calls, he found bullet holes in the wall above his bed and splinters of wood showered over his blankets. A few of the boys had been playfully employing one another as targets. He erected a bulletproof screen of boards and sand to keep future stray slugs from hitting him as he slept.

Dr. Henry F. Hoyt, equally young and new to the West, checked into Deadwood's P.X.L. Hotel, where he shared a room with a Black Hills miner. The miner possessed the room from noon to midnight and the doctor from midnight to the following noon. One night a drunk came in and found another man in his bed in a rear room. Guns banged. Bullets flew through the flimsy wooden walls and richocheted over the sleeping doctor's bed. Both the quarreling men were badly wounded.

"I was about the only one who profited by that affair," said Dr. Hoyt.

He treated a badly shot-up arm. His patient paid him in gold dust. When the doctor took the dust to the bank, he found it was not real gold. After that experience with his first fee in Deadwood, he carried a bottle of testing acid with him.

Confronted with frequent wounds, many mining-camp doctors developed an extraordinary knowledge of anatomy and operated with remarkable skill. Dr. Beverly Cole successfully ligated the left common carotid artery of U. S. Marshall Hopkins after his stabbing by Judge Terry in a California brawl. He did so at a time of day when, as he said, "It was too dark to see by the light of heaven and too light for candles." The marshall's blood was almost all drained away before the artery could be mended, but he recovered within five weeks.

In 1860 Levi Cooper, another California doctor, resected three ribs and removed the breechpin of a gun from just below the heart of a wounded man. Dr. Erasmus D. Leavitt, practicing in the Salmon River country of Idaho, was called to treat a serious gunshot wound. He removed not only the bullet and fragments of clothing, but also parts of a pistol handle. At Virginia City, Montana, Dr. Jerome Glick operated by candlelight in a cabin to extract a piece of a pistol cap from Samuel Smith's eye. Smith's eyesight was saved.

Dr. Glick and Dr. Ira Maupin of Helena sometimes rode out on calls together. One winter's day they galloped to Oro Fino to find three badly wounded men lying in the snow. "Professor" Hodge, manager of the mine, and a rival named Moore had simultaneously shot each other near the heart. Hodge's son had been hit in the wrist. The doctors carried the wounded men into a cabin where the temperature was below zero. Young Hodge's wrist was too badly shattered to be saved. While Dr. Maupin administered chloroform, Dr. Glick amputated his arm midway to the shoulder. Dr. Maupin stopped the flow of blood from the professor's chest, and Dr. Glick probed for the bullet without luck. There was nothing they could do for Moore, and he died. The professor and his son lived.

Lawless as the mining camps may have been, the countryside around them was even more lawless. Bandits infested regions where a pouch of gold could easily be picked up at pistol point from a lonely traveler. In some places miners gave the doctor their gold dust to take to the nearest express office, secure in the knowledge that no bandit would dare to molest the man whose services he might desperately need at any moment.

Once Dr. William Eichelrath of Aurora, Nevada Territory, was stopped by a masked gunman as he rode down the trail.

"Hands up and hold 'em high!" shouted the bandit.

"What the hell do you want of me?"

"Oh, it's you, Doc," cried the bandit. "Go ahead."

Neither Dr. Charles Cole of Helena, Montana, nor the bandit who accosted him one dark night showed such restraint. The bandit demanded the doctor's watch and money. Cole refused. The bandit fired a bullet into his left wrist. Cole pulled a gun and shot him in return. The bandit fled. Cole went home and bandaged his wrist.

Soon a messenger rode up and asked him to come to the aid of a wounded man. The doctor rode to a remote cabin, where he found the very man who had tried to rob him. He removed his own bullet from the man's abdomen, and the bandit got well. Thoroughly tamed, he became the doctor's stableman in order to pay his bill.

One March day in 1863, Henry Plummer, handsome Montana bandit leader, was shot in the trigger arm by Sheriff Henry Crawford. Dr. Jerome Glick was led to the bandits' hideaway where he saw that the bullet had entered back of Plummer's elbow and passed down the arm, breaking both bones and making his wrist useless. He advised amputation, but Plummer would not agree. Two of his men pulled out their guns.

"I just thought I'd tell you that if Plummer dies, I'll blow your head off," said one.

Dr. Glick painstakingly pieced together the fractured bones. The bandits kept him in the cabin with their leader until he was well on the road to recovery. By May Plummer had regained the use of his shooting arm and could go gunning for the sheriff.

In many mining camps fighting with knives was considered bad form. Six-shooters were the approved way to settle a quarrel, and Dr. George A. Kenny filled half a coffee mug with bullets he dug from miners at Salmon City, Idaho. Sometimes a doctor himself got into a gunfight. Dr. William Eichelrath argued with the editor of the Aurora, Nevada, *Times* over a dog. They adjourned to the nearby California-Nevada line where one stood in the state and the other in the territory so that no legal authority could stop the duel. Stout Dr. Eichelrath weighed in at 220 pounds; the editor was a six-foot bean pole. Yet the doctor clipped a piece out of the shin of the editor and ever afterwards enjoyed a reputation for sharpshooting.

A popular San Francisco newspaper editor, James King, was treated more cruelly by the medical profession. He was shot in 1856 by a gunman named Casey. Four of the top doctors of northern California removed the bullet, while the Vigilance Committee stood by ready to hang Casey in case the editor died under the knife. The wound was neatly sewed up, and everybody was confident the editor would recover. Unhappily, one of the attending surgeons left a sponge inside his body, and he expired. A bard of the Golden West set the story to verse:

Who killed cock robin?
I, says Dr. "Scamon."
With my chloroform and gammon,
I killed cock robin.

Why was it given
In a smothering dose, by heaven?
I refuse to say,
Replied Dr. Gray.

Who put in the sponge?
I, says Dr. "Lunge."
They did me impunge
So, "bedad," I left in my sponge.

Who blabbed the whole?
I, says Dr. Cole.
It lay on my soul,
and I blabbed the whole.

Dr. Beverly Cole did indeed blab the whole, and his loud charges of malpractice leveled against his fellow surgeons reverberated in poetic form through the mining camps. Miners, who had no desire to play cock robin in a sequel, stayed away from doctors if they could. When a lad had his leg mangled by a falling rock outside of the Rich Bar camp on Feather River, rough miners nursed him for six months rather than turn him over to the doctor. Finally, when his injury was compounded with typhoid and erysipelas, they called in Dr. Fayette Clappe, who forthrightly amputated the rotting limb and saved the youth's life.

Accidental injuries were even more common in mining camps than bullet wounds. Men fell down shafts, were crushed by boulders and blasted by exploding powder. Dr. Fred Peterson at Calexico, California, and the town druggist jogged together on burros to a remote desert mine where they crawled along a tunnel seventy feet into a mountain and another seventy feet down to the side of a miner who had been tamping powder with his left hand. A spark had set off the charge, shattered his hand, and brought the ceiling down. The doctor boiled the instruments in a kettle of water and successfully performed the surgery; the druggist then took the kettle and cooked their meal in it.

Drunken accidents were frequent too. When Dr. James Tyson reached Sacramento after his trying sea voyage from Panama, his first case was a miner who, whooping and yelling with alcoholic enthusiasm, fell and dislocated his lower jaw. At Bear Town, Montana, Dr. Armistead H. Mitchell was called to care for Shorty, who had fallen into a fire and crisped his left arm. The doctor went to Joaquim Abascal's store and saloon, where Shorty and his friends were waiting for him. Three planks were placed on whiskey barrels to make an operating table; Shorty was regaled with several long drafts of the barrels' contents as an anesthetic. When the doctor finished cutting off the arm with the aid of a common saw and a butcher knife, he cauterized the stump and wrapped it up in an old rag. He also wrapped the severed arm and set it aside to take home with him in the morning as a scientific specimen.

All was made tidy, and Shorty bought a round of drinks for the whole crowd. In honor of the occasion Madame Louise brought her girls, and the doctor, the miners, and the girls settled down to a night of poker and dancing. It was quite a night, and the next morning, as the doctor rode home feeling the full throbbing agony of each step of his mule, he lost Shorty's arm, never to find it again.

Sometimes the doctor himself was the drunk. Seymour C. Day, who practiced medicine at Red Mountain City, Montana, without benefit of a sheepskin, not only tended the sick and worked a claim but found plenty of time to indulge in his hobby, hard liquor. To his credit he would not take care of a patient when drunk.

"No, got to wait until am sober," he would say and then dose himself with three tablespoons of black pepper mixed with whiskey to bring about instant sobriety.

Over at Helena, Dr. Joseph Claridge proved made of weaker stuff. He strode into the saloon one night and told the boys he could drink as many glasses of whiskey as they would buy him without getting drunk. He put down four large tumblers without stopping, stepped outside, and fell on his face. He died the next day, and the minors averred he went to his maker well preserved in spirits.

Many doctors, on the other hand, were teetotalers. When hard-drinking miners demanded that Dr. George A. Kenny take a drink, he grabbed the whiskey bottle and chased them around the saloon in a vigorous endeavor to show at one blow the deadening effects of alcohol.

Doctors dealt more kindly with ladies who enlivened mining-camp nights. The hurdy-gurdy girls picked up a broad spectrum of diseases from the men, ranging from syphilis and lung fever to the common cold, and repaid the contagious compliments in kind. Nellie Talbott, queen of Montana's Bear Town, was beautiful and cultured. Dr. Jerome Glick noted her persistent hacking cough. He prescribed a remedy and advised her to avoid alternate hot and cold and stay warmly clad. She took the doctor's medicine but for professional reasons ignored his advice. Her cough grew worse; her beauty faded. Deserted by her admirers, Nellie moved to Phillipsburg, where, exactly as if she were a creature of fiction, she ended her life as a scrubwoman.

Juanita at Downieville, California, came to a more unorthodox end for a pleasure girl. On the singularly alcoholic July Fourth of 1851 a drunken miner was stabbed to death in her hut. A kangaroo court tried Juanita for murder and sentenced her to be hung.

"You can't hang me," she announced. "I'm three months pregnant."

The court asked the town's four doctors to examine Juanita. Three of them declared against her, but Dr. C. D. Aiken said the girl told the truth. The miners promptly ordered the dissenting physician to get out of town in twenty-four hours. Poor Juanita tucked a posy in her hair, tossed her hat to her friends, smilingly adjusted her noose, waved good-by, and stepped out into thin air.

The minority of married women in the mining towns carried on the normal role of bearing and raising young. Dr. Theophilus Degen, who after his adventurous trip over the Oregon Trail settled in the gold diggings, specialized in childbirth in a place where few babies were born. As early as seventeen days before the expected date, he would move in with the family in order to be on time. He is said in his lifetime to have delivered three thousand babies without a loss. Bearded, stout, he never sent a bill to anybody and traveled about the Oregon digs in a two-wheeled cart made by a grateful husband. In his medical bag he carried a comb and scissors with which he cut children's hair.

Dr. Degen barbered because he was fond of children, but in the gold fields many doctors barbered because they could not earn a living solely through medicine. Dr. Thomas Flint kept a butcher shop at Volcano, California, for the same reason, and also weighed gold dust for miner-customers. Doctors operated ferries, hotels, and stores, drove stagecoaches and ox teams and served in barrooms and at monte tables. They were forced to do these things to earn a living while, at the same time, quacks grew rich with the miner's gold dust.

Many doctors threw down their scalpels and picked up shovels. Dr. Victor Jean Fourgeard, who had traveled overland from St. Louis with his wife and little son in 1847, made the first assay of the gold found by Marshall at Sutter's Mill and promptly went prospecting himself. When news of the find reached San Francisco, all three of the town's doctors headed for the gold fields. Fifteen hundred doctors from all over the country joined the California Gold Rush, not to practice medicine but to strike it rich. Of the thousand prospectors at Bannock, Montana, in 1862–63, twelve bore the title of doctor.

As prospectors, doctors proved to be originals. Dr. Monroe Atkinson traveled the Montana wilderness with a pack horse and "one or more companions." He carried a pair of field glasses. Riding along the canyon ridges he peered at distant rock formations through his glasses and declared, "There, the country does not look good."

"I never knew of his digging a hole or panning a pan of dirt," said James Stuart, another prospecting doctor. "On the whole he was about as lucky as some of us, who dig many holes and wash innumerable pans of gravel."

Few doctors became bonanza kings. An exception was Dr. Elbert P. Jones, who gave his name to Jones Street in San Francisco. He possessed bags of gold dust. When a certain light came in his eye, Dr. Jones would excuse himself from his friends and retire to his bedroom. There he spread sheets upon the floor and poured the gold dust upon them. He poked his bare feet through the glistening piles and let it shower in handfuls on his head and naked shoulders. This frontier Croesus would finish his worship of the god of gold by rolling in his wealth.

Health conditions in the Old West mining camps were scarcely ideal.

"I never saw so many broken-down constitutions as during my brief stay in California," said Dr. James L. Tyson.

California was divided into two districts—the northern quinine belt and the southern vaccine belt. Colds and flu swept through mining camps because miners worked exposed to cold water and weather and spent their recreation hours packed in saloons, dance halls, and gambling rooms, where they coughed and sneezed at one another and spat on the floors.

Alexander Majors, writing of his life in the Montana mining camps, said, "Exposure and not being able to guard against sudden changes in climate caused many to die of pneumonia and fevers. The greatest number of deaths for a while seemed to come from what was known as the 'sawdust-gang'. Their money ran out, and they had to sleep on sawdust floors of saloons."

Scurvy, typhoid, erysipelas, diarrhea, dysentery, rheumatism, malaria, and Rocky Mountain spotted fever, sometimes called the black measles, were common. Anxious to avoid subjecting a boon companion to a doctor's dubious care, miners sometimes undertook imaginative courses of treatment. A Mother Lode remedy for scurvy was to bury the patient in the earth with only his head sticking out. A traveler came across one entire camp buried alive except for a few men who had been given the job of keeping off the grizzlies and coyotes. To cure mountain fever miners downed huge slugs of whiskey, which may have been as efficacious as the rest, warmth, and frequent baths prescribed by the doctors.

Much as a prospector staked out his claim to the earth's wealth, the first doctor to arrive at a mining camp was permitted to stake out his claim on a medical practice. A new doctor who tried to practice in the town was viewed as a claim jumper. A Dr. Hullings was first into Placerville, California. He was tall and bulky and wore a black coat with a Mexican sash about his waist. That he did not have a medical degree and was generally too drunk to take a pulse did not shake the miners' loyalty even when a degree-bearing English doctor arrived in town.

Dr. Edward Willis, a graduate of the University of Edinburgh, set up a tent to serve as his office and living quarters. A piece of sailcloth divided his residence from his surgery, where he installed pine shelves and an unplaned table. Splints, a jar of leeches, a microscope, stethoscope, implements of dentistry, chemical retorts and alembics stood upon the shelves making a mute but eloquent bid for the miners' favor. Dr. Willis hung up a sign: SETS BONES, DRAWS TEETH PAINLESSLY, BLEEDS, ADVICE GRATIS. The miners stayed away.

One day Dr. Hullings stalked into the sailcloth surgery followed by a gang of truculent miners. He demanded to see the doctor's diploma. Studying the document an instant, he tore it in half. Then he deluged his rival's face with a well-directed stream of tobacco juice. The miners grinned with satisfaction when Dr. Willis called Dr. Hullings outside to fight a duel.

There could be only one end to the matter when rough-and-ready Dr. Hullings faced the fancy Limey doc. The guns blazed, but it was Dr. Hullings who dropped dead! Dr. Willis' first act as Placerville's new physician was to sign his opponent's death certificate.

Dr. Willis' tent surgery was typical of the offices of most California mining camp doctors. Dr. Fayette Clappe's office at Rich Bar was described by his wife as a "beautiful architectural idea embodied in pine shingles and cotton cloth." Dr. Stillman's office at Sacramento was fashioned of boards ripped from dry-goods boxes and was six feet wide and twelve feet long.

The first mining-camp hospitals were equally jerry-built. When Dr. James Tyson set up a hospital at the Dry Diggings on the South Fork of the American River, he strapped a hundred yards of cotton duck to his saddle, handed the loose end to the cook, and rode until the material was spread out. The cook and the doctor felled some slender pines to hold the cotton duck from the ground.

The doctor had scarcely put the impromptu roof in place when a prospector from a canyon came to him dizzy and sick with typhoid. By evening he admitted two patients with dysentery. Next day twelve Oregonians carried a man on a litter for six miles to the hospital.

Doctors Morse and Stillman built their Sacramento hospital of sturdy wood, which was fortunate, because the flood of 1849 deluged the first floor. As the water rose, the doctors carried their patients to the second story. Tents, houses, boxes, barrels, horses, and cattle swept past the hospital. Dr. Morse, writing a letter home, said he poured brandy in his ink to give spirit to his thoughts while his colleague poured laudanum into his ink to quiet his apprehensions as he made out his reports.

The courtroom where the West's rough justice was meted out often provided equally dramatic "theater." When a doctor was called to testify, every man in town was sure to be on hand. Dr.

Gardiner in Colorado treated a man who cut his wife's throat and then slashed his own in a vain try at suicide. The doctor testified against the wife-killer.

"I will get you, you damned doctor!" cried the defendant, and lunged toward him.

In a wild melee the physician, the judge, and eleven of the twelve jurymen all whipped out their pistols. The twelfth juryman tugged frantically at his gun, which had caught in his suspenders. The defendant was subdued without bloodshed, and the judge gave him a fifteen-year prison term. Then he addressed Dr. Gardiner.

"Doctor," he said, "we have all heard the threats this prisoner has made to kill you, and I wish now to state before this court that if at any time you may meet this prisoner, you have the sanction of this court to kill him at sight."

This struck the miners as hard-rock justice.

"That's right, Judge," they shouted. "The doc sure has a killing due him."

Dr. Don Lorenzo Byam of Nevada City, Montana, made sure that no such fatal encounter would come up after the 1863 trial of bandit George Ives. The miners placed wagon boxes in the middle of Main Street to make a dusty outdoors courtroom. Dr. Byam presided as judge. When the jury found Ives guilty, the doctor sentenced him to be hanged. Then he supervised preparations, watched the fatal drop, and pronounced the bandit dead of a broken neck.

Mining-camp doctors encountered odd afflictions made worse by neglect. In 1867 Dr. Glick removed a seventy-foot tapeworm from Luke Byrne, a Bear Gulch, Montana, miner after he had treated himself with purgatives, vermifuges, and whiskey until he was too weak to dig. Dr. Thomas Reece of Helena traveled to nearby Unionville to treat a man and his wife who were seriously ill. He inquired as to what they had eaten and was told ham. Taking the ham to his office, he placed it under his microscope and discovered trichinae in the fibers. Soon everybody in town filed in to look at the specimens. Sales of ham ceased in Helena, and the butchers threatened to run the doctor out of town.

When Frank Talty of Summit, Montana, his wife and toddler, and their neighbors fell violently ill after dinner one night, Dr. Allan Fowler was called. He learned that Talty had pounded ore and placed it in a pan containing mercury to separate the gold. Mercury fumes had impregnated the food and poisoned the family and their guests. The baby died, but the adults recovered.

Another all-too-common disease of miners was silicosis. This was particularly true in the Rockies, where tunnels were forced through the mountains to get at gold deposits. Hard-rock miners at Central City, Colorado, died at an average thirty-eight years of age. Dr. H. A. Lemen of Denver described such a sufferer, whose health failed while working on a mining tunnel in Jones Mountain. He was emaciated, coughed and sweated a great deal at night, and ran a temperature of 103 degrees.

"He was expectorating daily large quantities of fluid, a specimen of which I exhibit you in this bottle," said the doctor, addressing the infant Colorado Medical Society. "He not infrequently expectorated a pint and half to two pints of this fluid in 24 hours. His pillow case and shirt bosom were bespattered with what looked like black ink. The sentence that I am now reading was written with this fluid. The pen used has never been in ink."

Rattlesnake bites were frequent in the mining fields too. Dr. Fred Peterson of Calexico, California, noticed that snake bites in the mountains were more virulent than those received in the valley. To treat the victims he opened the wound with his knife and injected it thoroughly with a potassium permanganate solution. Dr. J. Praslow, a touring German physician, and a mining-camp colleague, Dr. Asa Clark, were called to the aid of a Placerville man, who had been struck by a rattler. They found the man thoroughly drunk as the consequence of enormous amounts of liquor given to him by his friends to combat the poison. The doctors cauterized the wound with a red-hot iron. The victim did not die either from the bite or the treatment, but Dr. Praslow observed the next day that he had a ghastly hangover from the whiskey.

Often the doctor and his doings provided a mining camp with its most exciting entertainment. Dr. Charles Fox Gardiner took an enormous cystic tumor from a woman. It was so huge it pulled her scalp over until it dropped to her shoulder. As the doctor prepared to operate, a miner shoved his way into his office.

"I'm a-going to tell the folks how things is going," he announced.

Seating himself on the window ledge, the self-appointed commentator told the crowd outside what the doctor was doing.

"He's a-cutting into it," he cried. "He's got it roped and hogtied."

The doctor kept his scalpel at work.

"She's a-doing fine, folks. The Doc's giving her a drink. It's all over but the shouting."

The crowd yelled its approval and fired off a volley of shots. Everybody hurried Dr. Gardiner to the saloon to celebrate the feat of surgery.

A mining-camp doctor was accustomed to long hours and long miles. A Sacramento physician started Sunday, June 21, 1868, at 4 A.M. Before he went to bed that night between 10 and 11 P.M., he had worn out three horses to make a total of 100 visits to 87 different families. Only the toughest horses could stand a dedicated doctor's pace. To get such a horse Dr. Gardiner tamed a wild bronco with whiskey and mash until it was so docile it followed him about as if it were a dog. When a drunk threatened to shoot his horse one day, the doc pulled a gun on him.

Dr. William L. Treacy, Three Forks, Montana, was equally fond of his horse. One night thieves stole all the mounts in town, including the doctor's. Late the next night there was a rap on the grieving doctor's door. It was a messenger to lead him into the mountains where a man had been shot. The doctor shook his head. He could not go; he had no horse. The night rider said he had an extra horse, and the pair rode far into the hills. A sentry challenged in the dark. Dim figures huddled around glowing embers.

When Dr. Treacy had completed cutting the bullet from the wounded man, he looked about him and saw his own horse in a corral.

"That's my horse," he cried, and he stubbornly refused to go back to town in spite of the gang's darkest threats until his horse was returned to him.

For long hours, for riding through wintry blasts and fording the swollen streams of spring, for treating miners in distant canyons and bandits holed up in their lairs, most mining-camp doctors charged fees which were the equivalent of a miner's wages for the amount of time expended. In Montana the fee for an ordinary prescription was ten dollars in gold dust. A doctor charged two dollars for each mile he rode into the wilderness. Most doctors scaled these fees down to meet the ability of the patient to pay, but some expected every last dollar. Miners sometimes had to "chip in and raise the dust" to pay a companion's doctor bill, and it was said in the gold camps that M.D. after a man's name meant money down.

California fees were somewhat higher, and one physician, Dr. Richard Den, who failed as a miner at Sullivan Diggings, earned a thousand dollars a day treating malaria and dysentery. There were many who claimed Dr. Den was more of a bandit than he was a doctor.

At least few would maintain that Dr. Den was as much of a bandit as was Dr. Thomas D. Hodges, who presided over the life-and-death bet which opened this chapter. Dr. Hodges, not satisfied with his medical practice, robbed stagecoaches on the side. He developed a lightning "cross-navel draw" which shaded the fastest triggers among the guards. Then in 1855 he was captured and sent to Angel Island.

Dr. Hodges adroitly sucked in his cheeks to make them hollow, induced himself to vomit frequently, and fainted several times a day. The authorities took him to the prison hospital, at which he arrived apparently comatose and near death. Left unguarded for a moment, he jumped up and walked out of his room. The "sick man" knocked a guard senseless with one blow of his fist and sauntered out of prison. From then on he was known as "Tom Bell," the scourge of the open road.

But as he helped himself to the stage passengers' wealth, he remembered he was a doctor. One day a member of his gang shot a man who was reluctant to part with a belt full of gold. The victim fell to the ground, crying out in pain.

"Keep your nerve, man. All you need is a physician," said the bandit leader. "I happen to be a doctor myself." He took out his Bowie knife, dug a bullet from the flesh of his victim, tore strips from his own shirt, and bandaged the wound. Unable to leave an injured man in the wilderness, unable to take him with him, the bandit-doctor was in a dilemma. Fortunately a wagon rattled up. Dr. Hodges took ten dollars from his pocket and gave it to the teamster to cart the wounded man to town. Then he mounted his horse and galloped off with his men in search of another stagecoach.

Chapter XIII

COWBOY DOCS

Cowboys sat tall in the saddle and were too tough to die. At least so it would seem, judging from the memoirs of doctors who practiced among the ranches of the Old West. Take the eastern Oregon bunch grasser named Bill, whose horse kicked him in the forehead, right beneath his shaggy hairline. The hoof stripped a three-inch piece of scalp clean from the skull all the way from his forehead to the back of his head.

Bill tied the strip of flesh back in place with a red bandanna and rode eighteen miles through sub-freezing weather to Farewell Bend. Blood ran down over his eyes and froze in cakes on his face. He strode into Dr. Urling C. Coe's house.

"Sew up this goddam fool head o' mine, Doc," he drawled, "'fore all them damn little brains o' mine falls out."

Dr. Coe cleaned and shaved the cowpuncher's head and put in thirty stitches while the cowboy laughed, joked and told tall tales. By the time he had finished, the temperature outside had fallen to near zero. Doc thought maybe his patient might want to bed down for the night; instead he saddled up and rode forty-five miles to a ranch where he had promised to help out with the roundup.

Accidents in the corral and in the bunkhouse were frequent on frontier ranches. Dr. Charles Fox Gardiner rode along on western Colorado roundups because so many accidents were expected. Ranch records are chockful of injuries such as these two entries jotted in the log of the CY Ranch near Caspar, Wyoming, by foreman Robert M. Divine:

"Ben Lacey got hurt. his horse fell and his foot hung and he was drug for some distant. He is pretty bad hurt, but I think he will be all right for a week or so."

No doctor was needed for Ben, which is just as well, for no doctor was within a long day's ride. Soon afterward the foreman noted down another accident:

"Lee Divine is bad hurt. Horse fell with him. I am with him. Can't leave him. He is dangerous and is not liable to get well. Lee has something like spasms."

No doctor reached Lee either. Doctors were spread thin on the range, and many a stricken cowpuncher had to fight for his life with only a fellow cowboy to help him. When Dr. F. J. Bancroft began practice in Colorado in 1883, the nearest doctor was 140 miles to the east. Dr. Bancroft was the only physician in 8000 square miles of rugged, mountainous territory.

Trying to care for the sick and hurt scattered over such immense regions, cowboy doctors racked up cross-country riding records that rivaled those of the Pony Express. Dr. J. E. Hodge, Slim Buttes, the Dakotas, regularly rode 50 to 60 miles to the bedside of a patient. Dr. Urling C. Coe was accustomed to covering 80 miles of Oregon bunch grass country in a day; he clipped off 35 miles in three and a half hours over rough trails. When the Christmas tree caught fire in a hall crowded with ranch families at Silver Lake, Oregon, scores were fearfully burned. Dr. Bernard Daly rode 100 miles through the snow from Lakeview to find 38 victims already dead. He treated 36 and saved all but 5 with the assistance of cowboy nurses. Another Oregon doctor, F. C. Harley, Canyon City, rode so fast over primitive roads that he had to carry his hat in his hand to keep it from blowing away. Once he made a horseback call 250 miles away in Winnemucca, Nevada, and probably established the long-distance record for a cowboy doctor riding to his patient.

Harley's ride through the mountains was an epic, but he could not have covered the ground as fast as Dr. Bacon Saunders of Bonham, Texas. Dr. Saunders was always noted for his fast pace. Then one day he made what old-time Texas cowboys claimed was the fastest ride any doctor ever made. Doc was puffing on a cigar

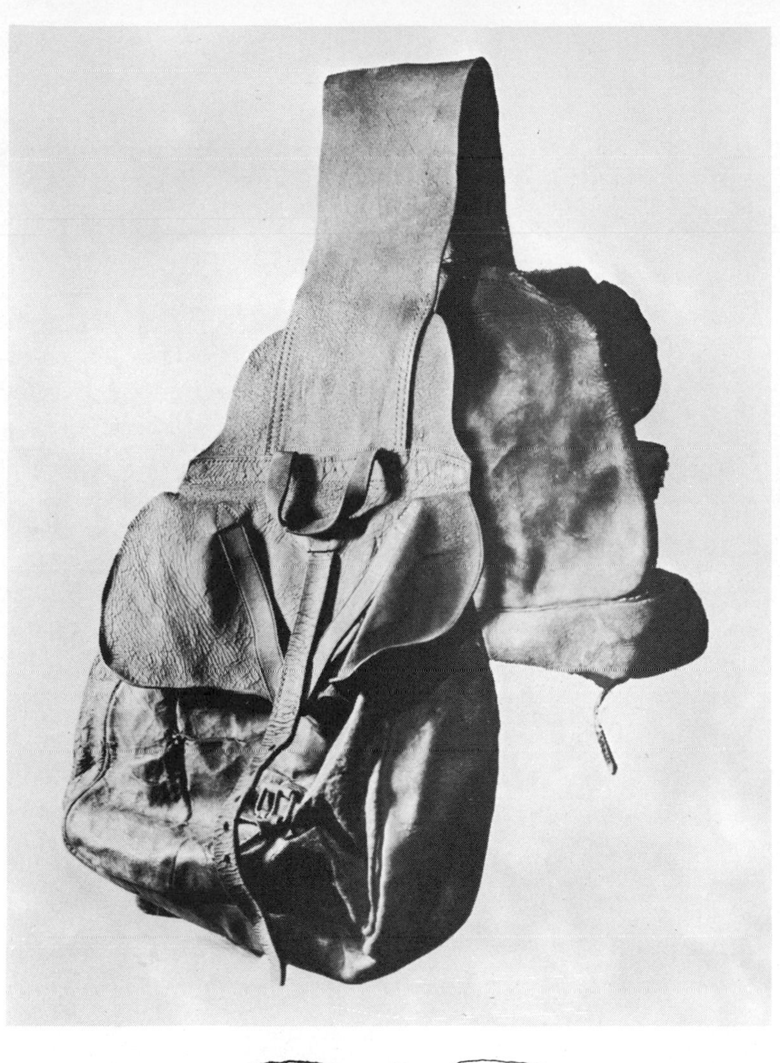

14. Dr. Whitman's saddlebags
Presbyterian Historical Society

15. A frontier doctor's saddlebags and surgical pocket kits were things of beauty to the afflicted. *Museum of Medical Progress, Prairie du Chien, Wisconsin*

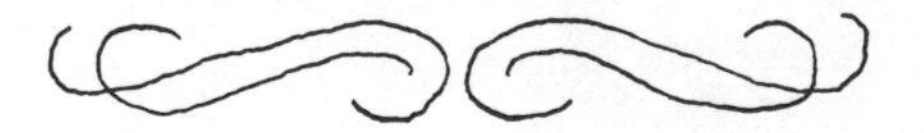

16. Frontier doctors used lancets to let blood when fever afflicted a patient. *Howard Dittrick Museum of Historical Medicine, Cleveland*

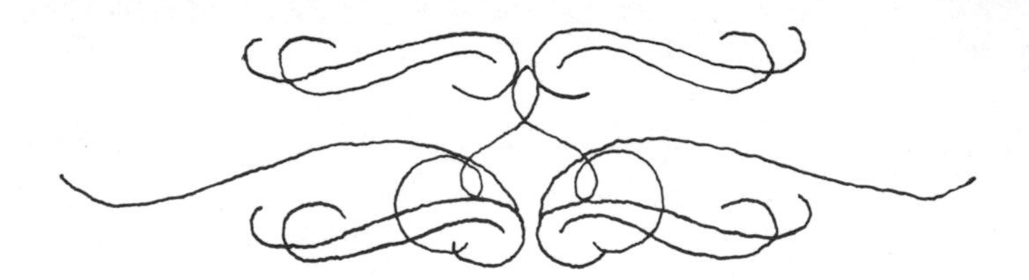

17. McDowell Apothecary Shop
Department of Public Information, Commonwealth of Kentucky
Photo by Kalman Papp

as his horse trotted home from a case. The horse kept increasing its speed—faster, still faster, until it was galloping furiously. The surprised doctor heard a roaring noise behind. Turning, he saw that his coattail was streaming fire, set ablaze by a spark from his cigar. The doctor, who coolly performed one of the first appendicitis operations in the United States on a family dining table with instruments sterilized on the kitchen stove, just as coolly halted his horse and beat out the flames. It was too late to save his coattails.

Dr. J. J. McDonald of LaGrande, Oregon, lived over a store. Neighbors grew used to hearing a horse gallop up in the night. The rider would alight on the platform before the store, his boots making a mighty thump which roused the doctor from bed.

"What must I take," sleepily asked the doctor from his second-story window. "Sleigh, wagon, or saddle horse?"

By the time he had thrown on his clothes, the doctor expected the appropriate transportation to be ready at the hitching post. Dr. McDonald also fixed up a stagecoach as an ambulance to bring injured cowpunchers back to town for care. One day he drove his ambulance eighty miles to a ranch to pick up a foreman.

"I won't ride the blamed thing," said the foreman. "It's too derned soft."

He insisted on riding beside the doctor on a buckboard.

Doctors rode horses and mules and drove buckboards and buggies. Dr. Juliet E. Marchant, a rare lady doctor, her black bag in hand, plodded on foot through the Texas mud around Lenox to make her calls. In the winter some doctors, fortified with bitters, took to snowshoes and sleighs to get through the drifts; others put their trust in sturdy cow ponies the year around.

One winter Dr. Thomas G. Maghee, the army surgeon who retired to private practice at Rawlins, Wyoming, was called to see a patient 60 miles away on the Snake River. With the temperature 40 below zero, Dr. Maghee rode until he was nearly frozen. Then he dismounted, caught hold of his horse's tail and literally ran for his life. Dr. H. A. Wright of Klamath Falls, Oregon, and his nephew employed their own version of Dr. Maghee's survival trick. In the dead of winter they drove a wagon for 110 miles in twenty-four hours. They took turns holding the reins and running behind, holding onto the tail gate to keep warm. On another trip Dr. Wright was thrown from his horse and his leg was broken. Crawling to a fence by the road, he tore out a board, fashioned it into a splint and fastened it to his leg. The doctor remounted and rode 12 miles to his patient, who, he knew, needed medical attention more than he did.

Dr. John G. Patterson was another Oregon doctor who was hard to stop. He set out over a rough road from Merrill to Bly in a sleet storm. A violent jolt tore the frame from the wagon bed, and the doctor was left bouncing over the ice on the axle. His clothes congealed to his back as he rode—a medical Ben-Hur in a Wild West chariot. Five hours and twenty minutes later he rattled up to a lonely ranch where he found a cowpuncher suffering cruelly with urinary retention. He had not brought a catheter, so he boiled the stem of a corncob pipe in a bichloride of mercury solution and inserted that to tap the swollen bladder.

On the trail a cowboy doctor slept on the ground, a blanket for his bed, a saddle for his pillow, his rifle at his side, and the bright western stars as companions, just as the cowboy did. He also had a cowboy's deep-seated love for his horse, as young Herbert Hoover found out. The boy, Bertie, lived with his uncle, Dr. Henry Minthorn, at Newberg, Oregon, in the Willamette Valley. His duties included feeding the doctor's team of ponies twice a day and hitching them up when the doctor set out on his calls. The boy was also expected to keep a half barrelful of water for the horses to drink.

Late one night Dr. Minthorn arrived home to find no water for his horses. He marched up the stairs, roused the sleeping future President from his bed, and sternly told him to go out to the pump and draw a drink for his faithful friend. From then on Bertie had to keep the barrel filled to overflowing.

Cowboy doctors had ingenious ways to make as many calls as possible on one trip. Dr. E. B. Hammock of Grant County, Oregon, rode a bluish pinto horse with odd markings, so that people could spot him at a distance and request his help. Dr. William Walker in Texas glanced at certain stumps as he galloped along the road; Fayette County ranchers knew that if they needed Dr. Walker, they should put a note on the stump and weigh it down with a stone. Dr. Charles Race, farther west in Uvalde, was on the lookout for cowboys waiting along his route to guide him up the canyons to hidden ranch houses. In Oklahoma doctors left their itineraries with the town druggist so that he could send a messenger after them in an emergency.

When he reached the ranch, a doctor often found his patient had been badly hurt in a fall from a horse. Dr. Ernest Crockett in Oregon galloped out from town to a young cowboy who had been eviscerated by his saddlehorn when his horse rolled on him. As another cowboy applied the chloroform, Dr. Crockett sewed up a large, U-shaped wound. Later peritonitis set in; the boy's abdomen bloated, and the stitches pulled out. The doctor inserted croton oil into the wound every hour until life-giving peristalsis began. Once the bowels were working, the doctor sewed up the wound again. The cowboy recovered and, to the doctor's chagrin, left the country without paying his fee.

Amputating a badly mangled arm with a meat saw and a butcher knife, setting painfully dislocated shoulders, tending broken legs and concussions, the doctor undid as best he could the damage done by the cowboy's broncos. Frequently the doctor stayed on at a ranch to nurse a patient who was critically ill. Sometimes the rancher gave him no choice but to stay. Dr. Samuel J. Crumbine, Dodge City, Kansas, rode thirty-five miles to a ranch to care for the broken leg of its owner, who had been tossed from his bronco. It was a simple fracture, and with the help of the foreman, the doctor handily set the bones. He prepared to ride back to town.

"Stay here," said the owner. He ordered the foreman to hand a Springfield rifle to him and then pointed it at the doctor.

"Jim," he said, "take good care of the doctor's horse; see that he gets a good night's rest."

"But I have patients in town," protested the doctor. "I'll be back here day after tomorrow."

"If you stay here tonight, you will."

The doctor stayed. In the morning the rancher, feeling much easier, handed him a generous cash fee and sent him on his way.

Gunshot wounds in some parts of the range were as numerous as injuries from riding accidents. When a rustler shot a range rider for the A-Bar-A in western Colorado, Dr. Charles Fox Gardiner rode to the scene. On a desert mesa he injected a shot of morphia into the arm of the cowboy, whose right rib had been smashed by a .45 bullet. The doctor washed his hands with a bit of soap and water poured from his canteen into a Stetson. He cut away the wounded man's shirt and took out the splintered bone. A cowboy held onto each of the patient's arms to keep him quiet. Flics buzzed around the patient; the wind blew dust over him. One of the cowboy nurses fainted and dropped the hurt man's arm. The only antiseptic the doctor had was whiskey, and he made free use of that. Finally the operation was completed.

Some of the cowboys rode off into the desert to gather firewood for the night. They rigged a blanket shelter; they joked outrageously at the wounded man's expense, but, said Dr. Gardiner, their every action was kind and gentle.

Sometimes a cowboy, though badly hit, would ride to town to find the doctor. An Oregon rancher was struck by a .45 Colt six-shooter slug, which was deflected by a big white button on his flannel shirt downward through his right kidney. He drove ninety miles to town in a buckboard to see Dr. Urling Coe. Bleeding copiously, he arrived in shock, but the doctor was able to fix up his wound. No sooner had the last stitch been put in than the cowboy got back in the buckboard.

"I wanna git back there an' shoot a button off o' tha shirt of that S.O.B. that shot tha button off o' mine before he has a chance to change his shirt," he cried, and the buckboard was off whipping up a rooster tail of dust.

One day a cowpuncher was brought to Dr. F. J. Bancroft's house by his brother. The doctor looked at the leg, which had been mangled by gunfire, and decided he must operate. A crowd quickly gathered. As the doctor sawed through the bone, the brother pulled out his six-shooter and waved it in his general direction.

"I'll kill this butcher doc if my brother dies," he told the crowd.

Dr. Bancroft smiled a tight smile and went carefully about his job. When he was finished, an onlooker asked, "How come you weren't scared, Doc? That boy meant business."

"I too had a gun," said the doctor, and his tight smile returned for a moment to his face, "and I would have been the first to know if death was imminent."

Range wars sometimes raged over whole counties; sometimes there were bitter feuds between single families. Dr. Gardiner found himself involved in a feud of the vest-pocket variety. As he rode up to a cabin near the Snake River in Colorado, he considered the pigsty on one side, the corral on the other, the smoke curling from the chimney and thought it a peaceful scene, even though he knew a sick boy lay within. Only when he dismounted and approached the gate did he notice that the wooden shutters were closed and the cowhide door fastened tight.

Zing! A rifle bullet smacked a stone beside the gate. On the piney ridge, the doctor saw a puff of smoke.

"Must be some damned deer hunter," he thought.

A second bullet spewed gravel on his boots. He was the target! Quickly he drew his gun and took cover behind a fence post. A cabin window was thrown open.

"You crazy idiot, get in here!" someone shouted.

He sped through the door with another rifle bullet in whining pursuit. Within doors he learned that he had arrived in the middle of a feud. Even so, he set to caring for the boy who was lying on a cot, delirious with smallpox. An old crone raved, bullets cracked into the thick logs, and the old man ran to the door and fired wildly up the hill. A bullet from the sniper on the ridge nicked the tip of the old man's chin and shot away a fistful of his beard. With a cry the crone gathered up some cow dung and made a poultice, which she started to apply to the wound. Dr.

Gardiner gently pushed her aside and cleaned the chin with carbolic acid and water.

At sundown the feud ended for the night by mutual agreement. Undisturbed, the old couple did the chores. That night the doctor slept on the floor beside the boy, jumping up to help him when he cried out with the fever. Pigs grunted; bugs chewed the doctor's legs. In the morning the doctor was pleased to see his young patient out of danger. He rode away from the cabin. No sooner had he mounted his horse than a bullet whined out of the woods at the cabin. The armistice was over, and the siege was being renewed.

Range doctors usually responded to a plea for help from rustlers and horse thieves. Dr. Coe, answering a night summons, galloped forty miles into a blizzard. Weary and nearly frozen, he at last reached a cabin and tumble-down barn sheltering at the base of a butte. There he collapsed in the driving snow. When he regained consciousness, he was wrapped in a blanket before a small iron stove which glowed with cherry red spots.

"Get some of this coffee into yer innards," urged a bass voice.

Dr. Coe soon learned he had ridden to the relief of Tex, a wounded horse thief, who lay in a bunk nearby with a gunshot wound. The coffee revived the doctor, and he got creakily off the floor. Still wrapped in his blanket, the doctor gave the wounded thief a hypo of hyoscine, morphine, and cactine. While Grizzly, a member of the gang, held up a lantern, he probed for a soft-nosed rifle bullet which had entered the left arm halfway between the elbow and shoulder and splintered the arm bone. He found a second bullet had struck the right leg above the knee, had penetrated upward, and had come out in the groin. The leg leaked pus.

As he stitched and dressed the arm wound, the doctor trembled with cold. Tex's eyes blinked open, and he cursed the doctor viciously for the pain he was causing. Going outside into the storm, the doctor tore a pine shake from the barn roof. He made it into a splint. As he swabbed out the wound in the leg, the man swore even more viciously.

For a few days Dr. Coe tended the injured horse thief. When he was confident the man would recover, he blackened his own face and even his eyelids with charred wood taken from the stove. This, he knew, would help break the fierce glare of the sunlight bouncing off of the snow-clad mountains. He rode back to town, conveniently forgetting that he had given succor to a man whom most other men in Farewell Bend would gladly have strung up to the nearest aspen.

Dr. William Routh, practicing at Peoria, Texas, had a similar experience with a medical call on horse thieves, but he had reason later on to rue his night's work. Scott Cooley and Bill Hudspeth, desperadoes, led him thirty miles through the night to treat a wounded member of their gang. When he was done with his scalpel, the bandit leaders offered him double his usual fee. The doctor accepted only what he regularly charged. As the day dawned, a thief escorted him out of the camp and along the road to town.

"That's a fine horse you've got there, Doc," he commented several times.

Dr. Routh thought this flattering, coming as it did from a man who, despite his defects of character, at least could be counted on to know good horseflesh. He was not so flattered the next morning. During the night somebody had broken into his stable and stolen the horse.

A jeweler of Schulenburg, Texas, suffered a fate that was proof that an innocent bystander to a cowboys' fracas was often the injured party. He was shot in the abdomen while standing outside his store. Friends carried him indoors and laid him on the floor. When Dr. William Walker arrived, he fainted at the welter of blood. After he revived, he was helped in caring for the jeweler by a three-year-old girl who wiped away blood as the doctor removed fragments of a watch and chain blown into the body. He sewed up the perforated intestines, and the jeweler lived.

An operation performed by another Texas doctor, C. W. Trueheart, was perhaps less dramatic, but it was a striking demonstration of frontier medical skill. A young man had received the full blast of a shotgun in his left shoulder at short range. Cleaning the wound of gun wadding, fragments of clothing, and shot, the doctor applied skin grafts. The wound finally healed except for the clavicular region where a three-inch gap in the bones allowed the shoulder to droop.

Dr. Trueheart rounded up a collection of healthy dogs. Nine weeks later he removed the granulation tissue, and between the ends of the youth's bones he inserted small periosteum and bone grafts taken from the dogs, which he chloroformed for the purpose. Eight out of ten grafts took. In two months the incision was healed; the clavicle was the correct length, and the shoulder did not droop.

The same old frontier diseases afflicted the cowboys as struck the mining camps. Mountain fever continued to confound the doctors, who did not realize it was sometimes malaria, sometimes typhoid. They treated a victim with sage tea mixed with whiskey or dosed him with calomel. Later, when they learned to recognize typhoid, they taught ranchers to boil water to control the disease. It was finally checked when deep wells were dug. Typhoid lingered longest in Southern California, where ranchers depended on cisterns filled with water from irrigation ditches. Malaria responded to quinine, which became increasingly available as the years passed. Tuberculosis continued baffling, as did rheumatism. On the Texas plains dengue fever still was common.

"It contains more aches to the square inch than any known disease," said an anonymous ranch wit. "Your back feels as if it was made up of mosaic and every piece put awry. Limberger cheese is attar of rose by the side of the breath of a dengue patient, and the taste in his mouth is like he had feasted heartily on carrion crow well cooked in the concentrated essence of polecat."

Diarrhea was annoyingly common because of the lack of cleanliness and poor chuck-wagon provender. An old-timer suffering from a chronic case went to see a Southern California doctor. The doctor told him it was caused by his way of living and his bad habits.

"Yes, that's so, doctor," he agreed. "The chronic diarrhea is a very bad habit."

Smallpox remained virulent, but vaccination was beginning to turn back the disease. To some cowpunchers the ounce of prevention seemed much too heavy. Dr. Henry F. Hoyt was vaccinating cowboys at Fort Elliott in the Texas Panhandle. Just as he was finishing up, the superintendent of the LIT Ranch walked into the store where the doctor was wielding the needle. He smoked a cigarette and yarned as he rolled up his sleeve. The doctor inserted the needle; the rancher looked at the tiny drop of blood oozing from his brawny arm and fell to the floor in a faint. The cowboys present allowed that such a perfect "shot" entitled the doctor to carve a notch on his gun.

Up in Montana, Dr. John Lewis Weitman of Great Falls was noted for his effective treatment of smallpox. His patients even recovered without scars. His explanation: "I get them so damned drunk they can't raise their arms to scratch the first three days."

Here and there cancer was being recognized by range doctors, and even on the range "where the deer and the antelope play," some cowpunchers managed to worry themselves into ulcers. Dr. Carlton Bacon of LaGrande, Oregon, treated a stomach ulcer with fresh cow's milk. In one case he had a cow tied to the chuck wagon, and it was milked for the patient's benefit. Ten days later the cowboy was breakfasting on ham and eggs.

Range doctors dealt frequently with hernias. Oregon doctor, J. R. Jonson, was called on a case of strangulated hernia. The sick man writhed in agony, and his abdominal muscles were so tense the doctor could not do a thing. He had no drugs with him and was as helpless as the crowd of sympathetic bystanders who had gathered around. One man squirted a stream of tobacco juice toward a spittoon.

"Bite off another chew," said the doctor.

When the man did, Dr. Jonson took the tobacco and inserted it into the patient's rectum. The nicotine quickly brought on a cold sweat and nausea. Muscles relaxed, and the doctor was able to reduce the hernia.

Doctors took out kidney stones too. Dr. Hillary Ryan, Galveston, Texas, had a patient who had passed a squirrel tail into his urethra. A large stone had formed around the tail where it was lodged in the bladder. With three boys assisting, the doctor cut into the perineum with a pocket knife and removed a stone an inch in diameter. A second operation was necessary.

"We passed the director into the bladder and made an incision into the urethra," reported Dr. Ryan. "Passed a probe in, as before, and made the cut in the same direction, to the left of the rectum. As soon as the cut would permit the finger to pass into the bladder, the director was withdrawn, and the finger used. The opening was enlarged very slowly and carefully until we had extended it for about two inches and a half; we then, with some difficulty, drew out a stone one inch and a half thick by three and one-half inches long, and in it the squirrel's tail, of about five inches in length, one and one-half inches bent back on itself. It was in a good state of preservation and looked very much like salted meat." The patient recovered quickly.

Appendicitis was rare enough to disconcert a cowboy doctor suddenly confronted with it. In eastern Oregon, Dr. J. H. Fell and Dr. James Ashfor diagnosed a cattleman's severe abdominal pain as appendicitis, but neither doctor had even seen an appendectomy. They anxiously questioned one another as to how the operation should be done. U. G. Cozad, bailiff of the court, overheard the doctors. He told them that a prisoner had committed suicide in the jail the night before.

"Maybe he had inflammation of the bowels," he said pointedly, and suggested a post mortem.

The two surgeons carried out the "post mortem," opened the dead man's abdomen, carefully reviewed their surgical technique, and planned their entry into their living patient. Satisfied with their dress rehearsal, they placed the appendicitis victim on a door stretched between two saw horses in a kitchen and successfully removed his appendix. They were so confident of their newfound skill that they had their young sons, both of whom were hoping to be doctors, observe the operation through the kitchen window.

Childbirth on an isolated ranch was often attended by midwives, sometimes with only a clumsy husband's assistance. Dr. Albert Rounsevell, Larimore, North Dakota, arrived at a ranch house to find a woman lying in a pool of blood. For days she had screamed and struggled trying to deliver a badly placed child. Her husband, mad from her suffering, had desperately seized a butcher knife and slashed open her abdomen to release a live baby. Swiftly the doctor sutured the uterus, closed and dressed the abdomen, and mother and child survived.

In Kansas Dr. Samuel Crumbine went to an isolated cabin to help a woman in labor. He found her lying on a blanket behind the stove while her bed was empty.

"The bed where a mother is going to stay for the next ten days must be as clean as possible," said her mother, "and I figured that this was the best way to keep it."

Dr. Fred Peterson at Calexico, California, found that the mother of one of his parturient patients was equally troublesome. Every time he put clean bandages on the new mother, the old woman replaced them with soiled ones as soon as he rode away. Once Dr. Peterson prepared to give chloroform to a woman whose baby was in a transverse position. She said it was unnecessary, that she had given birth to nine children without it. The doctor calmed her at last, and she kissed each of her children, who ranged from fourteen years down to two, and told them good-by. She pointedly ignored her husband.

Dr. Peterson put the woman on the dining table, and she delivered a six-pound boy, followed by another of about the same weight, and still another weighing a little less. Coming out of the anesthesia, the mother looked about her.

"Has the baby come?"

"Yes, all three of them."

"What," she cried. "I just knew that something would happen if I took chloroform. I'll never take that stuff again."

Ranch women were usually as rough and unwashed as their men. Mrs. Rouch, who lived near Helena, Montana, was rawboned and large, and she wore a man's hat, coat, denims, and high boots. Dr. William Steele rode out to her ranch to care for her sprained ankle, which she had bathed in hot water. He took one look at her horny foot and cried, "This is the dirtiest damn foot in Montana!"

"I'll bet you five dollars it isn't," she replied.

The bet was made. Mrs. Rouch pulled the boot off of her other foot, which had not seen soap and water for years, and won the wager.

Some doctors were temperamental. Dr. Belitha Powell, pioneer physician of Houston, Texas, suffered excruciating pain from rheumatism. One day he gave a patient a remedy for the same affliction.

"Take that medicine," he finally shouted, "and if it does you any good, let me know and I will take it myself."

Dr. J. W. Haines of Lafayette, Oregon, was, to say the least, blunt. He was treating an old lady for tuberculosis.

"Doctor," she said, "you know I can't get well. Why don't you just tell me so?"

"Why, goddammit, woman!" he exploded. "If I were you, I'd be glad to die. You are old and ugly as hell."

When a man in the last stages of cancer of the jaw came for a morphine treatment, he confided in the doctor that he would like to kill himself.

"Goddammit, so would I," said Dr. Haines. "Take the whole bottle."

Two days later the dying man returned with an empty bottle. Without a word the doctor handed him two bottles.

Dr. A. S. McDaniel strode the streets of San Antonio, Texas, wearing a high hat and a Prince Albert coat until someone pointed out that any dude wearing such fancy duds was highly susceptible to lead poisoning. Dr. Granville Phillips of Tyler, Texas, was a transplanted Kentuckian who pursued foxes, replete with baying hounds and hunting horns. Dr. Carroll Peak, Fort Worth, occasionally grew irked at being the only doctor in a bumptious cow town. He would hang his hammock in a grove of trees out of sight of his house, so that his wife could truthfully tell callers that he was not in.

When illness struck the doctor, he was usually hundreds of miles from medical assistance and had to cure himself. Dr. M. F. Honan was a Bellevue graduate who practiced in La Grande, Oregon. One day he suffered terrible abdominal pains, diagnosed his condition as appendicitis, and operated on himself. He died under his own knife. He learned too late that he suffered not from appendicitis, but from an infected gall bladder with gallstones. Dr. George W. Mason of Klamath Falls, Oregon, proved more successful at self-surgery. As he was riding back to town on the California Road after tending to an injured freighter, his buggy wheel dropped into a muddy rut. The doctor was thrown from the seat so that his leg caught in the spokes of the wheel. The frightened horses bolted, and the doctor's leg was almost twisted off above the knee before he could bring the team to a halt. Knowing that only an immediate amputation could save his life, he cut off his limb and bandaged the stump with a silk muffler.

Even a tough-hided old cowboy doctor died finally. In death he usually remained true to type. Dr. I. A. Davenport in Oregon died in 1874 and requested that his horse and saddlebags be buried with him. Down in Texas Dr. Sofie Herzog, rare lady doctor beneath western skies, laid down her scalpel for the last time. When they put her in her casket, they placed a necklace she had worn beside her weary bones. It was made of bullets which she had spent a lifetime digging out of gun-toting cowboys.

Chapter XIV

WILD WEST SAWBONES

George W. Parsons kept a diary in Tombstone, Arizona, at the time when this uninhibited mining town was called "the condensation of wickedness." One night he wrote down the following:

"Tonight about eleven-thirty Doc Goodfellow had just left, and I thought couldn't have crossed thc street. . . . when four shots were fired in quick succession from very heavily charged guns, making a terrible noise, and I thought were fired under my window under which I quickly dropped, keeping the adobe wall between me and the outside until the fusillade was over. I immediately thought Doc had been shot. . . . He had crossed through and passed Virgil Earp who crossed West side of Fifth and was fired upon when in range of my window by men, two or three of them. . . . I was just retiring, taking off my stockings . . ."

George Parsons, standing there, stockings half off, might have spared himself worry for his friend, George Goodfellow, M.D., because the gunfighters' surgeon lived a charmed life, miraculously escaping the frequent storms of bullets that swept Tombstone's streets and saloons. He patched up the lucky survivors and performed post mortems on the not-so-lucky dead.

Virgil Earp, seriously wounded by the gunfire as he strolled in front of the Eagle Brewery saloon, walked to the Oriental saloon to tell his brother Wyatt what had happened. His brother swore softly and took him to his room in the Cosmopolitan Hotel, where Dr. Goodfellow discovered one bullet had struck just above the left elbow, causing a longitudinal fracture of the humerus. Virgil also had a wound in his back; though it made him grit his teeth, it was not likely to be fatal.

Virgil's wife Allie, white-faced and trembling, watched the doctor working over her husband. She later said:

"I stood lookin' down on him and watched Dr. Goodfellow cut off the rest of the shirt. Then I almost fainted. A load of buckshot had hit him in the back, scalin' a little of the backbone. And then I saw his left arm! It was worse. A load of slugs had hit him in the elbow."

Virgil looked up at his frightened wife.

"Never mind," he said. "I've got one arm left to hug you with."

Dr. Goodfellow strove to stop the bleeding, which was leaking the gunman's life away. When he had succeeded, he prepared for surgery.

"Wyatt," said Virgil, "when they get me under, don't let them take my arm off. If I have to be buried, I want both arms on me."

Dr. Goodfellow took out four inches of splintered bone from Virgil's elbow as well as a great charge of buckshot.

"He'll live," he told Wyatt, "but his left arm will never be much good again."

Wyatt knew he could take the doctor's word as final. Years of repairing wounds inflicted by six-shooters and rifles had given Tombstone's leading surgeon an almost uncanny insight into what a man's prospects for recovery were. It was scarcely a cheery prognosis, but at least things looked better than the last time the doctor had been called to attend one of the Earps.

It was a night in March 1882, and Morgan Earp and Bob Hatch were playing billiards in Campbell and Hatch's billiard parlor on Allen Street. Morgan chalked his cue stick. Wyatt Earp sat in a chair and watched him. Suddenly two shots exploded through the glass panes of a door which led to the alley. The first shot dropped Morgan and streaked across the room and lodged in the thigh of George Berry, who was standing by the stove. The second shot cracked into the wall over Wyatt's head. The assailants fled.

Seeing that Morgan was badly hit, Bob Hatch carried him into the card room and laid him on a lounge. When Dr. Goodfellow arrived, the wounded man was gasping for breath. He had been shot in the right side of the abdomen; the bullet had passed through his spinal column. The doctor turned to Wyatt and shook his head.

"His spine is broken. He's done for."

Morgan stared feverishly around the room. His mind flickered from the terrible pain in his back to the pool game and back again.

"Don't, I can't stand it. This is the last game of pool I'll ever play."

He died, and the doctor turned his attention to George Berry. To his dismay he soon died also.

"Berry's injury was inconsequential," noted the doctor later, "and hardly more than an abrasion. Technically, he died from shock. The simple fact was the man was scared to death."

Probably no American doctor in civilian life ever had such a remarkable opportunity to perform surgery on gunshot wounds as did Dr. George Goodfellow, who was lucky and brave enough to be doctor-on-the-spot in one of the Old West's most violent towns, the town that ever since has been called, "too tough to die." Fortunately for medical science, Dr. Goodfellow was not only a talented surgeon but also a first-class medical observer, and even as he was saving lives he was making notes for brilliant articles which, unknown to the gunfighters he doctored among, appeared in nineteenth-century medical journals. It is interesting to speculate as to what the Earps and their trigger-happy companions in Tombstone would have said if they had known that they were being written up in such articles as, "Cases of Gunshot wound of the abdomen treated by Operation," and "Note on the Impenetrability of Silk to Bullets." Dr. Goodfellow had this to say about gunshot wounds:

"In the many autopsies made on the bodies of those killed during our reign of terror in 1880, '81, '82, I never failed to investigate the nature of the abdominal wounds, and have as often failed to find a vessel of any size cut. When a vessel of any size is injured, death is practically instantaneous. I have frequently seen men shot in the abdomen, fall and die within 15 or 20 minutes; opened the cavity, expecting to find some large-sized vessels cut, and discovered nothing more than the free border of an intestine torn for a foot or so."

Dr. Goodfellow learned that a wound in the abdominal cavity almost invariably led to hemorrhage and death in from fifteen minutes to only a few hours at the most. Abdominal section offered the only hope. He concluded:

"It is inexcusable and criminal to neglect to operate upon a case of gunshot wound of the abdominal cavity. This, by the way, applies more particularly to the West, where the caliber of weapons used and the amount of powder behind the ball is greater than in the East. The 44 or 45 caliber Colt revolver, cut off or long, with the 45-60 and 44-40 Winchester rifles and carbines, are the toys with which our festive or obstreperous citizens delight themselves; and it may be stated as a truism that, given a gunshot wound of the abdominal cavity with one of the above caliber balls, if the cavity be not opened within an hour, the patient by reason of hemorrhage is beyond any chance of recovery, and this without anything injured of greater moment than vessels of capillary size or a trifle larger, in either mesentery or intestine."

Dr. Goodfellow's stocky build suited him to be Tombstone's doctor. So did his adventurous temperament. He was born George Emery Goodfellow at Downieville, California, two days before Christmas 1855, the son of a sometime physician and mining engineer. At the age of ten he was sent east to Meadville, Pennsylvania, to live with an aunt and go to school. Later he was appointed to Annapolis, only to be discharged at the age of seventeen. He lost his temper, and with one blow of an already formidable fist, he knocked another cadet senseless down a flight of steps. He was graduated in medicine from Wooster University, Cleveland, Ohio, on February 24, 1876, married Katherine Colt of Meadville, and went back west where he practiced first in California, at Prescott and Fort Lowell in Arizona Territory, and then in Tombstone.

Tombstone was as two-fisted as the young doctor who swung down off the stage to hang out his shingle. Years before the cranky old scout Al Sieber had found Ed Schiefflin prospecting the area, hoping for a silver strike.

"Silver stones?" he warned. "You'll find nawthin' in them hills but yer own tombstone."

Schiefflin struck rich ore and called his claim "The Tombstone Mine." The silver rush was on, and Tombstone seethed with 15,000 get-rich-quicks, who simmered beneath the desert sun. Out of their frustration, discomfort, and boredom sprang bitter enmities which could only be settled with a six-shooter. Dr. Goodfellow himself felt undressed if he walked down the street without his guns dangling at his hips.

The Tombstone *Epitaph* of those days contained stories which showed why the doctor had every opportunity to become a proficient surgeon. On July 8, 1882, the paper told how Deputy Sheriff Phillips was killed while arresting a drunken Mexican named Filomono Orante who was flourishing his revolver in a saloon. As Phillips approached Orante, the Mexican stepped backward and stumbled. At the same time he whipped out his gun and fired. The bullet struck the deputy in the right shoulder. Swaying with the shock of the slug, Phillips put a bullet into Orante's thigh. Summed up the *Epitaph:*

"An express wagon conveyed the Mexican to jail. Dr. Goodfellow dressed his wound later in the day and found that the bullet had broken the hip bone, passing through the rectum and inflicting a dangerous and probably fatal wound."

Phillips died in the saloon, and the *Epitaph* reported:

"A post mortem examination of the murdered man by Dr. Goodfellow, showed the nature of the wound to be as follows: The bullet entered the upper part of the right arm passing through the pectoral muscles in front of the armpit, entered the chest cavity between the first and second ribs; thence passing through the upper lobe of the right lung; thence through the upper left lobe of the lung, in the left side of which it lodged. Death occurred from hemorrhage into the windpipe and pleural cavities."

Dr. Goodfellow was accustomed to a frontier physician's lengthy journeys on horseback. On the morning of July 12, 1889, he rode back into Tombstone, fagged from eighteen hours in the saddle. He had ridden over ninety miles to Buckskin Frank Leslie's ranch in Horseshoe Canyon, where he found a woman shot to death and a man badly wounded in the arms and body, both the victims of their host's ever eager gun. One of his longest rides took him into Old Mexico, where his patient was not a gun-toting miner or cowhand, but a demure young woman, the wife of a wealthy rancher, who was giving birth to a baby. The gunfighters' surgeon proved equally skilled as a baby doctor. When a fine son was born, the joyous rancher rewarded the doctor with a spring wagon filled with gold coin. Doc rode back to Tombstone, pulled up in front of a saloon, and invited the whole town to join him in drinking up the treasure.

When he was not mending punctured bodies and limbs, he studied tuberculosis and possible methods of treatment. He was among the first surgeons in America to remove the prostate, and was skilled in operating on the appendix. When George Parsons was injured in the big fire of June 1881, as Dr. Mahlon Delp writes, "with much ingenuity, Dr. Goodfellow repaired the lacerations, elevated the fractured bones and resuspended the face in a head cast, with a perfectly acceptable final result." He even studied gila monsters; his last scientific publication was a brief note in *Scientific American* concerning the bites of the unsavory creatures. When an earthquake ravaged nearby Sonora, he rode to the rescue of hundreds of injured Mexicans. From then on Mexicans called him "El Santo Doctor" and made pilgrimages to his home. In gratitude the Mexican President gave him a fine horse and a silver double-headed eagle supposedly the onetime property of Emperor Maximilian.

Dr. Goodfellow witnessed hangings, legal or otherwise, sometimes as coroner, sometimes as a member of a lynching party of outraged citizens. When two hundred horsemen disarmed Sheriff Ward, took bandit John Heath from his cell, dragged him down Toughnut Street and strung him up to the crossbar of a handy telegraph pole, the doctor was present. As coroner he drew up this report for the coroner's jury:

"We, the jury of inquest, impanelled and sworn by the coroner of Cochise County, after viewing the body and hearing the testimony, find that the name of the deceased was John Heath, 32 years old, a native of Texas, and that he came to his death from emphysema of the lungs, which might have been and probably was, caused by strangulation, self-inflicted or otherwise, as in accordance with the medical evidence."

An autopsy report issued by Coroner Goodfellow proved even more appropriate. Called in to do a post mortem on a gambler shot down in an argument over a card game, he reported that he had done the necessary assessment work and "found the body to be rich in lead but not too badly punctured to hold whiskey."

When the McLowery-Clanton Gang took on the redoubtable Earps, aided by the homicidal dentist Doc Holliday in the celebrated battle of the OK Corral, Dr. Goodfellow was not at the scene. After the shooting was over, bystanders took the still breathing Billy Clanton to his office which was across the street and upstairs. As he lay dying the desperado murmured, "Pull off my boots. I promised my mother I'd never die with my boots on."

All that the gunfighters' surgeon could do for him was to pull off his boots.

The doctor rode out with posses to tend to the wounded. He took care of the injured and certified the dead in cases of unrequited love, robbery, and drunken altercations. Once he himself inflicted a wound. The Tombstone *Epitaph* headlined the story, "The Good Doctor in Trouble" and reported, "Dr. G. E. Goodfellow in Justice Easton's court this afternoon was held over on a charge of assault with a deadly weapon. He was fined for carrying concealed weapons."

The doctor had stabbed Frank White in front of Arby's store. He was fined twenty-five dollars. The doctor had other brushes with the law too. It was impossible for him to explain what he was doing with a horse that had a U. S. Cavalry brand on it. He was observed to be exceptionally fond of Tombstone's ladies and not unduly concerned as to their morals. He was rarely known to decline a drink, although he always maintained that a doctor should stop drinking when he could not get up in the morning and hold the points of two needles together without a tremble. Tombstone did not scorn his shortcomings; nobody expected the gunfighters' surgeon to be a paragon of virtue.

Let Dr. Goodfellow take scalpel in hand and few cared about his personal life. Sometimes he performed his operations under desperate circumstances. When R. A. Clark was wounded in a gunfight at Bisbee, he galloped to his aid. He reached his patient at midnight and reported matters in this way:

"Without delay he was put upon a table in the large dining room of a restaurant; the anesthetic administered by a barber; lamps held, hot water brought, and no assistance rendered by others—the abdomen was opened by a single sweeping cut—an immense quantity of blood poured out through the incision the cavity being full . . . this was flushed out with a gallon of hot water—the principle sources of the hemorrhage were found, which were the liver and the gastroepiploica sinistra of the great curve of the stomach. After perfect cleansing, the abdomen was closed, and the patient put to bed. He became conscious in two or three hours, but never rallied, dying from shock about 18 hours afterward."

It would doubtless have been scant comfort to Clark that his death at least helped Dr. Goodfellow to perfect his technique still further. Understandably enough, the victims of Tombstone gunfire might have taken even less comfort in that their wounds gave the doctor proof of the amazing impenetrability of silk to bullets. Writing in the *Southern California Practitioner* for 1887, Dr. Goodfellow recorded:

"In the spring of 1881 I was a few feet distant from a couple of individuals who were quarreling. They began shooting. The first shot took effect, as was afterward ascertained, in the left breast of one of them, who, after being shot, and while staggering back some 12 feet cocked and fired his pistol twice, his second shot going into the air, for by that time he was on his back. He never made a motion after pulling the trigger the second time, the pistol dropping to the ground with his hands.

"Half an hour afterward I made an examination of the body.

Upon stripping it, I found not a drop of blood had come from either of the two wounds received. From the wound in the breast a silk handkerchief protruded, which I presumed had been stuffed in by some friends to prevent bleeding. I withdrew it and with it came the bullet. It was then seen that it had been carried in by the ball."

On another occasion, Dr. Goodfellow recounted, a man was shot at thirty feet by a shotgun. His face took the blast. During the autopsy the doctor noted that he was wearing a red silk Chinese handkerchief around his neck. He found two buckshot in its folds, neither of which had cut a fiber of silk. In a third case a man was wounded at three feet by a 45-caliber Colt. The ball had entered the right side of his neck two inches below his jaw. He too was wearing a red silk handkerchief around his neck, and it was carried into the wound and left there uncut.

"This man," said the doctor, "recovered, though the carotid artery of the right side could be felt bared and pulsating in the wound. He subsequently told me that all the liquids he took passed out of the wound for some weeks. He is now I presume, pursuing his trade (cattle-stealing) on the border—if not in peace, at least in prosperity."

Shortly before noon, on September 24, 1891, Dr. John Charles Handy, the leading doctor in Tucson, was gunned down and critically wounded. Knowing he was badly hit, he insisted that the gunfighters' doctor be sent for. The Southern Pacific dispatcher wired for Dr. Goodfellow and arranged for trains to speed him to Tucson.

Dr. Goodfellow raced behind a livery team to Fairbanks where a wheezing locomotive awaited. He himself took the throttle of the narrow-gauge engine. Screeching around curves and lurching over shaky trestles with throttle wide open, the locomotive raced to Benson, where another engine and a caboose were ready.

As the train chuffed away from Benson, the doctor told the second crew, "Step aside, boys. We got to get up some speed."

He drove the train across the desert at a rail-shaking clip. The train came to a stop at the Main Street crossing in Tucson, only two blocks from Dr. Handy's home. At 8 P.M., less than six hours after he had received the summons, Dr. Goodfellow was tracing the bullet from where it entered the left side of the abdomen to where it emerged at the tip of the spine. The intestines clearly had been perforated. He had to operate.

He outlined the problem to the still conscious Dr. Handy. Did he wish to submit to an operation? Dr. Handy told the gunfighters' surgeon to proceed.

At 10:20 P.M., with the help of three Tucson doctors, he set about repairing eighteen holes in five feet of intestines. At 1:00 A.M., just as he was inserting the last suture, Dr. Handy died.

Dr. Goodfellow went back to Tombstone, but he did not remain long. He gave up his practice among the gunfighters. On his last night in Tombstone, his friends feted him at dinner in the Can-Can Restaurant. In the morning the surgeon left for Tucson where he took up the practice of the doctor whose life he had failed to save.

Chapter XV

RAILROAD SURGEONS

There is a grisly scalp in the Boys and Girls' Room of the Omaha Public Library. It is displayed in a glass case, and children, borrowing books, stop to gape at it. They shiver at the wavy blond hair with its reddish tint. What must it feel like to be scalped?

Union Pacific telegraph operator William Thompson could have told them, because the scalp in the glass case is his. He lost it on the night of August 6, 1867. That night the telegraph wires along the railroad west of Plum Creek, Nebraska, suddenly went dead. Perhaps a herd of buffalo had toppled a pole and downed the line, perhaps the wind had snapped it, or a wandering band of Indians had cut it. Railhead was already far out in Wyoming, so there seemed no likelihood of an Indian raid in force that far east. Thompson and four other men set out on a handcar to find the break and fix it.

During the afternoon, unknown to the railroad men in Plum Creek, Chief Turkey Leg and a strong war party of Cheyennes had slipped unseen past frontier settlements and forts and reached the vicinity. They had taken up strong positions in low hills along the track and then cut the wires. As one of the raiding Indians later said, "We got a big stick, and just before sundown one day tied it to the rails and sat down to watch and see what would happen."

The railroaders pumping the handcar down an incline did not notice the stick. When their flying car hit, it jumped the track, throwing the men to the ground. The Indians whooped from ambush and shot and knifed the crew. Thompson's four companions died. He was hit in the arm by a bullet. Stunned, he fell to the ground. Instantly an Indian leaped upon him and expertly cut and wrenched his scalp from his head. The Indian shouted and waved his bloody trophy in triumph. The knife tearing through his skin brought Thompson back to his senses. Starting up, he snatched his scalp from the warrior and ran away. The Indian, scarcely believing what had happened, stared after him but did not follow.

Pleased with the first results of their ambush, the Cheyennes now pried up some rails. Again they waited. Far down the track a column of smoke appeared, growing larger. They made out a high-stacked locomotive racing toward them. It whistled frightfully, but when the engine hit the rail break, it too plunged off the tracks, careened into a ravine, and exploded in a mass of flames. Freight cars were flung across the prairie.

The Indians broke into the cars and settled down to a wild costume party with barrels of whiskey to drink and bolts of calico, ribbons, bonnets, boots, and hats for finery. A second train came charging down the track, but its engineer saw the frenzied Indians ahead in time, braked to a stop, and backed furiously away from the scene. The train outdistanced a party of braves who galloped in pursuit. Finally, after a day's orgy, the Indians were preparing to leave when a rescue train loaded with Major Frank North's battalion of Pawnee scouts arrived at the wreck and hastened their departure.

The rescue train found Bill Thompson very much alive. He had put his scalp into a bucket of water. Thirty-six hours after it was removed from his head, he arrived in Omaha where railroad surgeon Richard C. Moore dressed the wound with gauze saturated with pure olive oil. Some old railroaders claim that the doctor attempted to graft Thompson's scalp back into place, but the doctor's report, which he read to the first meeting of the Nebraska State Medical Society on June 24, 1868, makes no mention of it. That the Indian who did the scalping knew his bloody business is attested to by the surgeon's description of the wound. The scalp was entirely removed from a space measuring nine inches from ear to ear and seven inches from the forehead to the back of the neck. There was also a severe tomahawk wound of the right parietal bone on the side of the skull and a slight gunshot wound through the fleshy part of the right arm.

Pink velvety tissue soon began to cover the tissue surrounding Thompson's denuded skull but did not cover the bone. In about three weeks the skull began to shed its outer layer. The wound took on a healthy appearance and within three months the entire surface was covered with a fibrous scar. Thompson went back to work for the railroad. Dr. Moore put his scalp in a glass case, in which it has remained as a grim reminder of the problems of railroading in the Old West.

Indian ambushes were common enough on frontier railroads that passengers were instructed as to what to do in case of attack. Railroads did not offer to provide travelers with "pistols if requested" as did some stagecoach lines, but they did print on their tickets: "Passengers must assist the conductor on the line or road whenever called upon." This might mean helping to drive buffalo off the tracks, jacking the train back on the rails in case of a derail, and fighting off both Indians and train robbers. With rail travel so hazardous, railroad surgeons were necessarily much in demand.

Most western railroads established emergency medical stations at division points and contracted for the services of local surgeons at way stations to give first aid. If a rail broke and snapped up through the wooden floor, chopping fearfully at the passengers, the surgeon bound up the wounds. He delivered babies in parlor cars, inspected sleeper cars, and healed all sorts of injuries received by the train crews.

Surgeons were in on western railroading from the start. They went on the expeditions which explored the routes to the Pacific. Dr. George Hammond accompanied General Isaac Stevens on his exploration of 1862. At Fort Owen he amputated the legs of a man who froze them in the bitter cold and saved his life. When the explorers and surveyers had mapped the way, the construction gangs set to work to push the rails into the wilderness. Accidents were frequent. As the Oregon and California Railroad was built through the Siskiyou Mountains, injured men were so numerous that Dr. John S. Parsons had his home completely filled with them.

Disease was a still more serious matter. Living in unsanitary camps, forty to fifty men in a tent or cabin, the men contracted typhoid. Ignorant of the thousands of Indian deaths caused by smallpox, the workmen often looted Indian burial grounds for buffalo robes wrapped around the dead. They caught smallpox themselves and spread the disease anew. Mountain fever was also common in the construction camps.

Not all construction camps could have a doctor. Cy Warman knew the construction camps of the Santa Fe Railroad firsthand. He recalled how feeding and housing the men went hand in hand with keeping them healthy.

"One of the first tents to go up in the grading camp is the hotel tent," he wrote in 1898, "and the man who runs it is the boarding boss. He is usually a jolly fearless man and a good hustler, but not necessarily addicted to real manual toil. His wife does that. From four in the morning until midnight, this slave of the camp is on her feet. To be sure, there are men cooks, flunkies and dish washers, but the boarding boss has but one wife, and she must oversee everything. If one of the drivers is kicked by a mule, she bathes his hurt with horse liniment and allows the wounded man to sit in the rocking chair in the eating tent."

Warman explained that the boss kept a medicine chest filled with medicated bandages done up in rolls and pinned ready for emergency use. He also stocked a few simple remedies, but for most injuries he employed spring water and horse liniment.

Once the trains started running the number of injuries increased. "I believe that the railroads furnish more material to the surgeons than all the wars," remarked Dr. Joseph Kurtz.

He wrote of his experience with railroad spine, a concussion of the nerve centers, and railroad brain, a mental shock caused by the jolting of the cars. Engineers were all too often scalded by the steam from their boilers in the frequent derailments and collisions. When hastening to the scene of a wreck, Dr. Kurtz said, "I start with a set of splints, plaster, a pocket case and an abundance of absorbent or antiseptic cotton and plenty of iodoform."

When the surgeon arrived on the scene of a wreck, according to

Dr. Frank L. Barnes, who practiced at Trinity, Texas, he must "arrest hemorrhage, relieve shock, prevent infection, dress and immobilize the injured part, make patient comfortable."

Sometimes the train left the rails with such force that even an unharmed passenger could not stand on his feet for hours after the wreck. Dr. J. T. Craven reported to the Colorado State Medical Society in 1881, "whether the man be thrown from a train in rapid motion, be crushed between cars or run over, the patient becomes pale, cold, faint and trembling."

Patients in this state of shock were wrapped in warm blankets, and heat and friction were applied to their extremities. They were given drugs such as morphia and atropia.

Field surgery under unsanitary conditions disturbed railroad doctors, since by the 1880s most of them were well acquainted with the nature of infection. Dr. Barnes cautioned his fellow railroad surgeons not to use water when wounds were "dressed in the depot or caboose or on the track where an adequate supply of sterile water cannot be obtained for the wound and the hands of the operator."

Doctors were often able to obtain an adequate supply of hot water by tapping the engine boiler.

They amputated limbs or fingers crushed by crude coupling devices, and they delivered babies. When the Santa Fe train rolled into Spearville, Kansas, one day, a woman was so far advanced in labor that the doctor did not dare remove her from the train. The brakeman shooed other passengers from the car as the doctor made a table by placing a plush seat back on the top of the coalbox in back of the stove. A female passenger was pressed into service as a nurse. The baby was born without complication, appropriately named Santa Fe, and the mother continued on west to her homestead.

Locomotives steaming down the tracks streamed clouds of gritty smoke from their stacks. Cinders flew in the open windows of the cars, and frequently lodged in the eyes of passengers and trainmen. Dr. R. H. T. Marin of Texarkana, Texas, generally found the cinder on the under surface of the upper lid and removed it with a toothpick wrapped in cotton at one end. Dr. W. C. Jones of Walnut Springs, Texas, used similar methods and criticized train crews who happened to have cocaine on hand. "They will put this in the eye," he complained, "then sharpen a match, or use the point of a pocket knife and proceed to remove the foreign body."

Amateur surgery on cinders impaired or destroyed the vision of many travelers and crewmen on the western railroads.

Many doctors were dismayed by the racket and jarring of the coaches as they rattled over the rails. Some maintained that rail travel was salubrious. Dr. Daniel M. Blount called a ride in a bucking coach, "passive exercise."

"Passive exercise has not received the appreciation at the hands of the profession that is justly its due," he said. "As an agent for the promotion of the health and spirit it is second to no other at our command."

Not one to expound an untested theory, Dr. Blount traveled 20,000 miles to prove his point. He claimed improved breathing, appetite, excretion, and sleep.

"Railroad travel by its constant jarring is continually subjecting the subject to a series of mechanical impacts," he said. "No particle of the nutritive fluids is allowed to tarry long in any one place in the system but is compelled to move on by an external applied force."

Dr. Blount, veteran of many a good night's rest in a tossing Pullman berth, had advice for sleeping passengers. He urged them to put on loose clothing; ladies were not to wear corsets. A traveler must "never be guilty of retiring without removing his shoes," should eat before going to bed and sleep with his head toward the engine.

When winter chill made it necessary to close the windows of the cars, the atmosphere inside became virulent. Cigar smoke, the odor of tar, discarded lunches, and dirty clothing, became so intense that many passengers sucked lemons as an antidote. Dr. Thomas D. Tuttle described conditions in frontier Montana railroad cars:

"The floors of the day coaches are covered with all kinds of filth. The tobacco chewer spits on the floor, the little boy throws his peanut hulls on the floor, the consumptive expectorates on the floor. All this filth and trash accumulates until the division point is reached. Then comes the brakeman with his broom.

"He is anxious not to lose a minute at the end of his run and he brushes this dread filth into a dust that is simply stifling; and this dust is laden with the germs of tuberculosis. The passengers must breathe it, they cannot get out of the car, and the law says they must not kill the brakeman."

Travelers risked food poisoning each time the train made a refreshment stop. Boys toted uncovered cans of impure water through the trains and sold drinks to thirsty passengers from a common cup. Typhoid was frequently imbibed with the water.

Whenever a physician traveled aboard a train, he could count on giving emergency medical attention to somebody before his journey was over. The military surgeon George Sternberg was on a train crossing the mountains, when a porter told him a woman was ill. She suffered from a poor heart and tuberculosis, and the high altitudes had aggravated her condition. When Dr. Sternberg reached her seat, she begged him to keep her alive until she could get home and see her children.

The doctor took the seat next to her and gave her medicine to counteract the effects of the high mountains. After the train rumbled through the highest pass, she felt better. Finally at a junction, it was necessary to transfer to another train. Dr. Sternberg asked for a blanket. Three other men and he lifted the woman on it; then each took a corner, and they carried her to the other train. Ten days later the doctor received a letter from her to let him know she had arrived home and seen her children.

To reach injured passengers or trainmen, railroad surgeons rode boxcars, handcars and engines. Dr. John Evans, himself a builder of railroads, was riding in an engine above Bailey's, Colorado, when an emergency occurred. As the train rounded a bend, the broad-shouldered doctor saw a terrified girl on the rails ahead. Realizing that the train could not possibly stop in time, he climbed along the locomotive to the cowcatcher. The doctor held onto the rod with one hand, leaned forward, and pushed the girl from the path of the train with his free hand. He considered the episode as preventive medicine.

Chapter XVI

SODBUSTER DOCTORS

"My ears were as fragile as candied fruits and my gloved fingers were freezing in my pockets," wrote Dr. Lewis J. Moorman, a physician who practiced among the sodbusters of Oklahoma, as he recalled his horse and buggy rides across the unbroken prairies. Buffalo were disappearing from the prairies and homesteaders were breaking the virgin sod, but hardship was still very much a part of a doctor's daily life during the last decades of the western frontier.

Dr. John Fear was called out of his Waverly, Kansas, home at 2 A.M. to ride through a snowstorm to an obstetrical case on a farm. His buggy stalled in five-foot drifts.

"I had a shovel and a hatchet in the buggy," he said, "and dug my team out and got them across the road and into a field on the north side. My next problem was to get the buggy out. Finally, by lifting the buggy one wheel at a time, I got it on top of the drift where the frozen crust on the snow bore it up and I pulled it over the fence."

The doctor drove on as the sweat from his exertions froze on his forehead. He arrived, shaking with chill, at the farmhouse in plenty of time to welcome a new Kansan into the world.

In spring sodbuster doctors still had to make their way across unbridged floods.

"If Caesar could swim the Nile and not get his 'Commentaries' wet, it appeared that I should be able to get across the Salt Fork and keep my cathartics dry," said Dr. Moorman.

He took the saddle from his horse and swam the animal across the stream. Cold water swept up to his armpits. At the end of his ride he found a woman suffering from a gallstone colic; he observed that her house was full of kids and her bladder full of stones. He was able to do something about the latter.

Chiggers, fleas, bedbugs—all skipped merrily into a doctor's hat or coat when he put them down on a bed in a nester's sod house. He dressed in the black morning of winter by the light of a coal-oil burner; he might scramble eggs in the buttered bottom of a clipped-off paper bag. Then he climbed on his buggy and rode off on his rounds. Chances were good that he would sleep that night on a bed of grass on the prairie. "Now I lay me down to sleep," Dr. Moorman customarily prayed, as he looked up at the cold stars. "Thank God for the Mackintosh."

A doctor still practiced scores of miles from his nearest colleague, and he still must cure his own ills. If he had a communicable disease, he isolated himself from his neighbors until he was well again. Now, at least, it was rarely necessary for him to attempt surgery on himself; railroads reached among the settlements, and except in an emergency he could travel to a bigger town farther east where there might even be a hospital. Even so, when Dr. William Mayo in Minnesota observed a sore on his mouth turn cancerous after three months, he readied his own instruments and needles and took a shot of whiskey. Seating himself in front of a mirror, he directed an assistant to cut off a piece of his lip. When the knife pared away the cancer, he shouted, stanched the bleeding himself, and stitched the lip.

There was still the clatter of hoofs in the night, growing nearer and nearer and ending at the doctor's door. He kept his horse and buggy ready to roll. Children, he knew, could suddenly grow violently ill, and if the summons was to the side of a sick child, he dashed away into the dark, anxious to get there before the family killed the small sufferer with treatment culled from one of the many medical books that could be found in every settler's home. Most doctors attended children first, then women, old men, adult males, and last of all "known hysterics."

As children became more numerous in the settlements, scarlet fever, measles and diphtheria spread among them. The mortality rate for youngsters ran tragically high. In Lawrence, Kansas, between 1870 and 1880 the average age of death was eighteen years. Fifty per cent of all deaths occurred among children under five years old.

On the high prairies people lived in soddies made of virgin buffalo grass sod eight to ten inches thick. The rude dwellings were warm in winter and cool in summer, but they were damp and poorly ventilated. Cattle, horses, sheep, and hogs were kept in pens and corrals near the soddies, and flies pestered animals and people without discrimination. There were no screens to keep them out of the house, and infant diarrhea, cholera infantum, cholera morbus, dysentery, and typhoid fever were common.

Settlers lowered buckets of milk and butter into their wells to keep them from souring, but the milk often sickened children. Sodbuster doctors urged parents to feed their infants on condensed milk, which was beginning to reach the general stores springing up at crossroads and in villages.

Schools were usually airless, oversized soddies or drafty structures jerry-built of boards brought from Wisconsin or Minnesota sawmills. Dr. N. H. Morrison, practicing among Russian settlers in Kansas, was disgusted with the extraordinary school they erected.

"For a floor they first put one thickness of board and then a layer a foot thick of manure and then another thickness of boards," he said.

The doctor considered the odoriferous school the cause when fifty children sickened of diphtheria and twenty-five died. If so, it was not the stench that was at fault, but the stale air and crowded classroom benches, which helped the disease pass from child to child. Other schools along the frontier were equally noxious contagion points for diphtheria. In Westminster, California, among the newly planted orange groves, seven of nine children died of the disease in ten days. Everywhere in the West diphtheria was the greatest scourge of children.

There was no antitoxin at that time, and doctors could only stir a teaspoon of sulphur or powdered brimstone into a half pint of limewater, boil the mixture for two hours and drop it into the patient's nostrils with a quill. Nature took its course, which meant that in laryngeal diphtheria the child almost always choked to death. Sometimes a courageous and desperate doctor slit open the small throat and opened the windpipe. Placing a handerchief over the wound, he sucked the deadly secretions from the larynx with his lips. When the child could breathe again, he sewed up the incision. On the way home the doctor chewed plugs of tobacco or slugged down a bottle of whiskey in an effort to keep the infection from reaching his own throat.

Among immigrant people who sewed boys into winter clothing for the entire season, and who bathed no more often, doctors frequently contended with skin diseases and insect infestations. Contaminated wells were often the source of typhoid fever. Although one Nebraska farmer's wife and eight children were all sick with the disease, he laughed at Dr. Francis Long's opinion that his well was unclean. Finally just to quiet the "crazy doc," he cleaned out his well and found a rotten corn cob and some corn husks, dead rats, mice, and a rabbit.

Ignorance continued sometimes to amuse, more often to anger, doctors. Dr. Ferdinand Herff, who practiced among Texas homesteaders, prescribed seven powders for a farmer's wife who was experiencing severe constipation. The price of the powders seemed high to the farmer, so he went home, and under the supposition that a powder is a powder, gave his wife seven doses of gunpowder instead. When the doctor stopped by to see how the woman was getting along, he found her no better and decided he must give her an enema. He told the farmer, "Bring me two chairs, a syringe, hot water and a lamp."

"Doctor, I bring you the chairs, the syringe and the hot water," said the farmer, turning pale, "but I don't bring you the lamp. That woman has seven charges of gunpowder in her."

The doctor told the tale for years afterward and never failed to chuckle with merriment.

Dr. Samuel Crumbine was not amused in the slightest by an incident in his medical practice. He was called to see a baby whose mother reported he was "acting very strange." The strangeness was death. The mother refused to believe the dread news. How could the baby be dead? He only had caught a very bad cold and cough. She had given him cough medicine.

"The child seemed to get worse," she said. "Then I gave the medicine more often and in larger doses. Then we sent for you."

The doctor explained that she had narcotized the baby with her ignorant home remedy.

A farmer near Enid, Oklahoma, drove his wife and children to work in the fields every morning with a whip. He lashed at their legs and backs whenever they lagged, until the sun went down. One day a pretty fifteen-year-old girl from the family came to see Dr. H. C. Bowers. The doctor clenched his teeth when he saw the cruel welts on her back. Climbing into his buggy, he rode out to the farm, seized the farmer by his long beard, beat him severely with his free hand and dragged him before the justice of the pcace for sentencing. Cruelty was common among settlers, who sometimes became almost demented by the harsh circumstances of their life.

On the other hand, sodbuster doctors' journals are full of stories of the kindness, generosity, and affection which tied families and friends together in the face of the droughts and dust storms, insect plagues, blizzards, and floods that nature flung at man on the plains. Even strangers might share a man's trouble. A family of Colorado nesters was stricken by typhoid fever. When the doctor arrived, he found a strange cowboy cooking at the stove.

"Howdy," he said, and never looked up from his frying pan.

He had already built a fire on the hearth, washed the dirty blankets, swept out the cabin, and scrubbed all the children. Stepping to the cabin door with a rifle in his hand, he fired at a buck on the far side of a lake and dropped it with a shot through the heart. The doctor watched the bowlegged cowboy amble over to his kill and drag it back to the cabin to furnish the sick family with a meat supply. As the doctor took temperatures and checked pulses, the cowboy rolled the sick people over.

"When a horse lies on one side too long, he gets bed sores," he explained.

As soon as the family was convalescing nicely, the stranger went away. He left in the night. In the morning each child found a beaded Indian belt by his cheek as a parting gift.

Surgery still tended to be dramatic in the last years of the frontier. Dr. Samuel Crumbine, practicing at Dodge City, Kansas, described such an operation:

"Arriving after dark at the home of a family that had called me in, I found a 12-year-old boy semi-conscious, blue and breathing with great difficulty. Examination revealed that the cavity on the left of the lung was filled with fluid, that the left lung was completely collapsed and that the heart had been displaced, pushed way over to the right of the chest.

"Wrapped in a warm blanket, the lad was laid gently on the kitchen table and I went to work with the father holding the kerosene lamp so I could see and the mother standing by to assist.

"I punctured the left chest. But when I withdrew the instrument I had used, the pressure was so great that the fluid in the boy's chest came out like a geyser, overshooting the basin the mother was holding. I was wearing one of her clean aprons as a surgeon's gown and was deluged. But there was no time to clean up, for the too rapid withdrawal of the fluid and the resulting release of pressure had been too great a shock for the failing heart. Happily, restoratives, heat and the determination to live that comes from a hardy constitution pulled the boy through."

Sodbuster doctors operated on threshers' mangled legs on a parlor sofa, the kitchen table, or the familiar door placed on sawhorses. They set fractured femurs with a piece of string and a flatiron. They executed podalic versions on the kitchen table. They still were men who brooked no delay. When Dr. William Mayo visited a Minnesota granger farm, he spoke to a small boy. The child replied with a twisted tongue.

"Why, that child is tongue-tied," exclaimed the doctor. "Come here, George!"

The boy climbed on his knee as Dr. Mayo took out a pair of scissors from his pocket case. The lad opened his mouth; the doctor snipped the membrane that bound his tongue. He gave the youngster an affectionate pat and sent him on his way. The boy used his untied tongue so well he grew up to be a judge.

As nesters homesteaded on the plains and in mountain valleys and fruit growers settled in lush California valleys, lumberjacks in the north cut timber in what was still wilderness forest. Typhoid fever and malaria were common among loggers. Mosquitoes bred in the woods, and the men drank untreated water hauled in barrels from the nearest creek. Accidents were frequent too. Dr. Harry R. Cliff, St. Helens, Oregon, had a great deal of experience cleansing and sewing up knife gashes.

Dr. Cliff was also the county coroner. Once a man was found dead from a knife wound in the back. The discoverer of the body and the doctor brought the victim to the doctor's drugstore. There they laid him on his back on a table. A crowd gathered, and the doctor questioned the loggers with the hope of turning up a clue as to who did the murder. He was getting nowhere. A half-breed got up and came over to the corpse. He raised a shoulder to peer beneath.

"Is the wound very deep?" he asked.

"Arrest that man and hold him!" cried the doctor.

He pointed out in true Sherlock Holmes fashion that only the man who did the knifing would know where the wound was.

Blizzards swept down out of the north, and farmers froze feet and hands. Doctors amputated when they had no choice.

In the hot summer Dr. Francis Long went to see the small son of a Nebraska saloonkeeper. The boy was ill with cholera infantum; his temperature was 104 degrees, and he was in convulsions. The sick room was stifling. Doctor and saloonkeeper together hauled a huge block of ice from the saloon beer vault and placed it in a tub in the middle of the room. The air temperature fell and helped to cool the burning fever. The child lived.

Not only ice intended to cool beer but medicine helped the doctor to save lives. Few doctors now searched the hillsides for herbs; few operated without anesthetic or antiseptic. Most doctors now had sheepskin degrees, and the newly established state governments licensed medical practice. A doctor still did not consider it beneath his professional dignity to take veterinary care of a farmer's livestock, although he was now getting a little testy about it. A farmer rode up to Dr. William Mayo's house and spied the doctor nailing down a new roof.

"Come see my horse," he said.

"Sure, I'll come," replied the doctor, putting down his hammer. "I'll look at a horse or any other damn thing you've got."

In the northern forests doctors paddled canoes on their rounds among the logging camps. On the plains most doctors continued to prefer their saddles to a horse and buggy. A horse or mule could follow cowpaths and ravines and ford creeks where a buggy could not. Doctor still made a picturesque sight as he sped to a patient's side. Here is Nebraskan Dr. George O. Remy's recollection of a neighboring sodbuster doctor, William B. Loomis, as he mounted and galloped away.

"As soon as the doctor's weight was on the stirrup, the pony was off. If the doctor lit in the saddle, all right, if not, he had to climb over into position as best he could as she ran, and run she always did.

"When you saw them coming, it always looked like a race with death or the stork. The mare running, the doctor pulling, his saddle bags straight out to the sides, and his long overcoat flying back over the pony's tail."

Dusty roads now linked farms to town, and doctor began to adopt newfangled transportation. In Texas Dr. R. A. Goeth, among others, gave up his horse for a bicycle. He assured patients, "If you have any trouble tonight, you just call me, I can jump on my bicycle and run over while the other doctors are hitching up their horses."

Young and better-trained doctors were arriving in the West. One talked to aging Dr. Lewis Moorman in Oklahoma. He told the old doctor that he simply could not see himself settling in Jet.

"What's the matter with it?" asked Dr. Moorman.

"Well, you can't expect a man to live in that place. There's not a bathroom in the whole town."

"When I was there," observed Dr. Moorman, "the closest one was in Wichita, Kansas."

The old doctors still kept their strange ways. Dr. Larkin Vanderpool at Dufur, Oregon, continued to deposit one hundred dollars in the bank for each baby he delivered who was named for him. They were to get the money when they came of age. When the doctor died his funeral procession was a mile long.

In Coquille, Oregon, old Dr. Walter Culin died too, and he was given the biggest funeral in the town's history. For scores of miles around when folks heard the old frontier doctor had gone, they worried, "Doc Culin is dead, and I don't know how I'll ever raise my baby."

A brilliant young graduate of an excellent school came to practice in Coquille. He went to see his first confinement case, a mother with several children playing around in the house. The woman wept as he checked her condition.

"Why are you crying?" he asked. "You're doing fine."

"I guess it must be because you are not Doctor Culin," she said.

It was 1893, and the U. S. Census Bureau said the frontier was closed. That the frontier no longer officially existed was not always evident to doctors practicing medicine in the West. There was no sudden end to hardship and danger, disease and suffering. People still were stricken by disease and fought to live. The medical frontier remained open even if the geographical frontier was closed.

Chapter XVII

QUACKS AND IRREGULARS

A cowboy named David fell ill in Galveston, Texas, and the "fever doctor" gave him opium. He always gave opium to his patients regardless of their complaint, and David's friends were not surprised. Considering the quack's results to date, they were also not surprised when as night approached David appeared to die.

The barber was engaged to shave the corpse for the funeral. The men wrapped David in a shroud, laid him on a carpenter's bench in an upstairs room, and retired below for a few rounds of drink. They recounted the deceased's many fine qualities and shed tears in their whiskey. At last they lifted their glasses to drink to David's safe journey into the next world. Just then there was a heavy thud upstairs.

"David has fallen down," said one mourner.

"Fallen down! How the devil can a dead man fall about?" cried another.

A fearful groan sounded through the ceiling. Everybody jumped up. Halting steps creaked down the staircase. The door opened, and David, wrapped in his shroud, stared at them with accusing eyes. He pointed to his parched tongue with his left forefinger and extended his right hand.

"Give me some brandy and water," he croaked.

His friends stampeded through the door into the night. David sighed, sat down to a table and finished the brandy bottle. In the morning he had a hangover, but he had recovered from the disease that had afflicted him. The quack's opium treatment had left him unscathed.

On the frontier even a quack as unskilled as the one who dosed

David readily found patients. A strange crew of irregulars, midwives, faith healers, folk doctors, and charlatans practiced in the settlements, the mining camps, and among isolated ranches. Even circuit-riding ministers in Kansas carried medicine cases in their saddlebags. Some of these practitioners were conscientious men who prescribed calomel, quinine, gentian, and jalap with something of a sheepskin doctor's knowledge. Dr. George O. Remy, a pioneer Nebraskan, paid tribute to these men:

"They were, of course, short on diagnosis and the finer action of drugs, but they were long on common sense and resourcefulness. They knew their limitations and when to call for help."

Nobody would say that the porter who turned doctor in Brownsville, Texas, knew his limitations. He prescribed sulphuric acid to "burn the pulmonary tubercles" of a woman ill with consumption. Two days later he buried her. He sawed the leg off of another patient with a butcher knife, and he died too. For bowel troubles he injected melted Spanish wax. Medical doctors protested, but the porter went right on practicing his drastic brand of medicine.

Even the Texas Rangers were not immune to quackery. In 1857 a ranger asked a pompous San Antonio quack to extract an iron Indian arrowhead from his head. The quack sneaked an anxious look at the mean guns in the hands of the ranger's friends and demurred.

"I cannot 'stract this, stranger," he said, "because to do it would go nigh killing you, but I can give you a pill that will melt it in your head."

In South Dakota in the 1880s two "doctors" showed no such qualms about surgery. A rancher was hit in the leg by a wild bullet at a party. The doctors—a druggist and a barber—consulted together and amputated. They were at least right about one thing. Their prognosis was that the man would probably not recover. He didn't.

The kindly shoemaker of Empire City, Oregon, also took to mending people's health. Once when his most strenuous efforts failed to save a woman's life, her husband asked what caused her death.

"Err-umph," said the shoemaker with a show of sapience, "tapeworm on the liver."

A doctor's patients sometimes deserted him for a charlatan. A faith healer came to pioneer Jet, Oklahoma, and wooed away the patients of Dr. Lewis J. Moorman. He finally moved in with one family, ate their meals, slept in their beds and infected everybody with the itch. The mother stopped by the doctor's office one day.

"Doctor, I want some medicine for the itch. The children are clawing the skin off their bones."

"That's strange. What's the matter with your faith cure?"

"It's all right, Doc, but it won't stop the scratching."

It took many refills of the doctor's prescription to cure the family. But he could prescribe nothing that would cure them of their willingness to place their health under the protection of the next smooth-talking pseudomedico who came down the road.

Certainly a smooth tongue was essential to a quack's medical practice. One urbane individual toured the frontier as a specialist in the diseases of women. Dr. Francis A. Long encountered him among the Nebraska settlements, where he claimed he had been a physician to the Queen of England. Dr. Long wryly observed that the Queen's own physician did not know a forceps from a bedpan. What medicine he knew he had learned as a fulminate mixer for the Union Metallic Cartridge Company at Bridgeport, Connecticut.

Some of the most colorful of the quacks traveled the early nineteenth-century trans-Appalachian frontier. The most extravagant personality of them all was "Doctor" Richard Carter. To cure debility he offered patients a selection of "Gold filings given in doses (night and morning in honey) about as much as would lay on the point of a penknife, bear's gall mixed in rum or chewing orange peels and swallowing his own spittle." He concluded his prescription with an appropriate disclaimer: "If any application is likely to do more hurt than good, it should be abandoned."

His sure-fire cure for gout, rheumatism, cramps, and infirmities of the sinews and joints probably should have been given up at the first hearing, but pioneers took the Doctor's incredible prescription to heart. Said Carter:

"Take a young fat dog and kill him, scald and clean him as you would a pig, then extract his guts through a hole previously made in his side and substitute in the place thereof, two handfuls of nettles, two ounces of brimstone, one dozen hen eggs, 4 ounces of turpentine, a handful of tansy, a pint of red fishing worms, and about three-quarters pound of tobacco, cut up fine; mix all these ingredients well together before depositing in the dog's belly, and then sew up the whole, then roast him well before a hot fire, save the oil, anoint the joints and weak parts before the fire as hot as you can bear it, being careful not to get wet or expose yourself to damp or night air, or even heating yourself, or in fact, should you not expose yourself in any way."

Dr. Carter became a celebrated authority on the hypo, that extreme hysteria of the frontier, which he attributed to ennui. It seemed to strike down men and women when more routine afflictions such as colds, fevers, dropsies, and gouts passed them by. People imagined they were teapots or had glass legs, and Carter cured them all with blood-letting, foot baths, injections, and dosages of calomel and aloes.

Once an old man came to him convinced that he had ballooned up beyond any human size. He told a sad tale. He had gone to bed in a room with a small boy. In the morning he tried mistakenly to get his foot into the boy's pants and fell to the floor with a crash. The household came on the run.

"What's the matter?" they cried.

"Why can't you see what's the matter?" he screamed back. "I'm swelled as big as an ox. I cannot get my big toe into my pantaloons."

Dr. Carter set the old man down in his case book as an example of the hypo. He soon had another case—a man who thought his belly was full of ducks. He could even hear them quacking. A bellyful of quacking ducks presented no serious problem to the doctor. He undertook to cure the man with a purge. As the purge did its work, he deftly popped a brace of young ducks into the basin.

"But how," asked the now relieved patient, "did the ducks get in my belly?"

Dr. Carter assured him that he "had eat a great many eggs in his time, which had collected and hatched." From then on the patient eschewed eggs, and Dr. Carter turned his attention to the case of a young man who, having been jilted by his girl, had sat for three months on a goose egg.

"If this was not the hypo," reported Carter in his case book, "it was very much like it, if not worse."

The doctor was also adept at determining if a woman was pregnant. One day he was feeling poorly and set aside a sample of his own urine to settle and left the room. One of his woman patients came in, poured out the liquid and filled it with her own urine so that the doctor could make the necessary tests. She neglected to tell the doctor, and when he made a laboratory test of the phial's contents, he was shocked to learn he was pregnant. He knew he was constitutionally unable to deliver the child and was greatly worried as to the ultimate outcome of his condition. Fortunately he learned what had happened before he applied the sort of stringent remedy to himself that he would have meted out to a patient.

Equally famous on the frontier, Dr. Constantine Rafinesque had nostrums for most illnesses. This self-proclaimed doctor, who was as brilliant as he was untutored, was born in 1783 in Constantinople, the son of a French merchant. Year by year through trial and error his remedies became more appropriate to the disease he was treating, until in some respects he arrived at sound medical practices, some far ahead of his time. While sheepskin doctors were treating pulmonary consumption with bloodletting, he built up his patient's health with a diet rich in milk, fruit and green vegetables, insured good elimination, and insisted on an outdoor life.

Rafinesque studied botany and zoology on the side and was

not above a scientific prank. He was a bona fide expert on fish and hoaxed Audubon into sketching a strange fish, which he maintained swam the western rivers. The fish was ten feet long and possessed bulletproof scales. Fifty years later scientists were still searching for Rafinesque's monstrous denizen of the river deeps.

He also had a disdain for the ubiquitous frontier crops of corn and pigs. He wrote a lengthy paper on the need for growing pearls in the Ohio River and concluded that then at least there would be a sufficient supply of pearls to cast before the settlers' far too numerous swine.

As the frontier moved on west, scores of other irregular practitioners managed to be in the forefront of medical thought for their day. A retired New England sea captain who practiced his own brand of high-seas medicine on the Kansas prairies was sent for by the family of a man whose foot had been torn open by lightning. The wound was not healing and was full of maggots.

"Let them alone," he said. "They are only carrying out the dead flesh and dead bone. They never attack anything that is living."

Later doctors inserted maggots into wounds for this very purpose.

Q. D. Smith of Cloverdale, California, had learned his medicine from boatmen and fishermen along the Tennessee River of his boyhood. At first he limited himself to herb cures and employed a decoction of willow to treat rheumatism, diarrhea, and malaria. By 1876 he was using antiseptic "bromo chloralum" on open lesions and observing a cleanliness that shamed nearby sheepskin doctors. He had an inventive turn of mind too and made a curved knife joined to a pair of sharp forceps to remove splinters. It folded up neatly so that he could carry it in his vest pocket. To drain an empyemic chest, he used a catheter attached to a pig's bladder.

Midwives and practical nurses usually could be found in remote communities where there were no doctors. A frontier woman irregular was expected to be hardy and resourceful, but none could match Nancy Rogers, a practical nurse near Wichita, Kansas. She disliked spending money too. When Dr. Henry Owens told her that her cancerous breast should be removed, she agreed, but she would not agree to his fee. She drove her wagon home and cooked enough food to last her family for a week. Then she packed a basket with her nightgown, some muslin rags, a parcel of food, and a butcher knife and said she was going away for a week's visit. In Wichita she rented a room for two dollars. Locking herself in, she sat on the edge of the bed and without any anesthetic, cut off her own breast with the knife. She lived and practiced for many years after her extraordinary surgery.

Most of the maternity work in the Old West was done by midwives. One woman in Jackson, Wyoming, delivered more than a thousand babies. As doctors arrived in the frontier towns where they practiced, most midwives welcomed them and co-operated in the care of the sick. This was not true of the midwife in Farmington, Utah, who had no use for young Dr. Ezra Rich. It was her custom to give a postpartum douche of carbolic acid or bichloride of mercury solution. The doctor's first patient was suffering from puerperal sepsis. She was a beautiful, black-eyed girl, reported the doctor, with a high fever, rapid pulse and in delirium. She was under the midwife's care when the doctor reached the house.

The midwife had told the girl's husband that she had taken cold. Under her direction all the windows were closed tight with quilts hung over them to keep out the draft. It was May, and the odor in the room was unbearable. Dr. Rich finished his examination and told the husband that a radical change in treatment was necessary.

"He said for me to go ahead with the treatment I thought best," said the doctor later. "I told the midwife what was necessary for her to do, instructing her to put ice packs on the head and abdomen, open the windows and institute other supportive treatment with vaginal douches. The midwife said that such treatment would kill any and every woman and that she would not be responsible for the results. She then walked out."

Under Dr. Rich's treatment the girl eventually recovered.

"This case was the talk of Farmington and Davis County," said the doctor, "and if she had not recovered, I would probably have been practicing in some other locality."

A Chinese doctor at Long Creek, Oregon, proved equally inimical to the efforts of Dr. Ernest Crockett. The father of a sick child called both the Chinese and Caucasian doctors to his cabin and bid each to effect the cure. Dr. Crockett diagnosed the illness as bronchial pneumonia. The Chinese felt the child's pulse and exclaimed, "Debil all time around. Catch looster, bury in ground, head out; looster lib three days, den baby lib. Looster him die, den baby die."

While the rooster suffered through three days of semi-interment, Dr. Crockett employed every medical weapon to save the child. Both the rooster and the baby lived. Dr. Crockett was chagrined when the father gave the credit for the child's recovery to the Chinese.

During the last decades of the frontier, some of the elderly irregular practitioners asked bright young doctors with medical degrees to take over their practices. When Dr. Henry F. Hoyt arrived at Bernalillo, New Mexico, to assume the work of aged "Doctor" Carroll, he was sick with a fever. The old irregular skillfully cared for his sick young protégé. When he had restored Dr. Hoyt to health, he confided that he was not actually a physician. He had never given anything but quinine, castor oil, and native wine, and he did not consider himself a quack even if he had no medical degree.

The old man packed up his simple equipment and prepared to leave town.

"Bernalillo," he said, "is lucky to have a real doctor now."

18. Surgeon Ames Walker Barber, stationed at Fort Fetterman in Wyoming Territory, poses with his horse and dog, a saddlebag doctor's best friends. *Western History Research Center, University of Wyoming*

19. Dr. McDowell's home in Danville, Kentucky, as it looks today. *Department of Public Information, Commonwealth of Kentucky*

20. Dr. Morrison, the physician in charge of the field hospital at the Northern Pacific's stampede tunnel construction in 1886, poses with his family and some of the men maimed in the work. *Northern Pacific Railway Company*

21. A frontier doctor's boots, coat, and hat wait by his desk for him to ride out on a call. *Museum of Medical Progress, Prairie du Chien, Wisconsin*

22. Patients were put to bed in this cabin, which in 1828 became first hospital in St. Louis. *St. Louis Medical Society*

Chapter XVIII

GRANNY MEDICINE

Malaria was so common on the mid-continent frontier that it was not even considered an illness.

"He ain't sick," folks said. "He only got the ague."

In Illinois in 1836 they say a family shook so violently with the ague that workmen shingling their roof felt the cabin tremble. A man might feel "languid, stupid and sore and down in the mouth and heel and partially raveled out," but he rarely saw fit to do more than apply one of the hundreds of sure-fire folk remedies available for virtually every affliction and disease known to man. Calling a doctor, an irregular practitioner, or even a quack was often out of the question because there might not be one in a hundred miles. Doctors were kept in reserve for a serious illness. Miss Prudence Smith, who concocted a "List of Family Medicine Recipes" for her 1837 book, *Modern American Cookery*—a best seller on the frontier and among families going West—described forty-three illnesses. She suggested that her readers call a doctor only in case of smallpox, inflammation of the bowels, nosebleeds, and gravel.

Grannies and mothers charged with keeping their isolated frontier families healthy believed in preventive medicine. Their methods were strenuous. Most believed that a person could preserve his teeth and eliminate mouth odor by rinsing his mouth every morning in his own urine. Longer-range protection for the teeth could be obtained by a mother who during her baby's first six months rubbed his gums with the rattle of a rattlesnake or the brain of a rabbit. A rabbit's tooth suspended around the neck also warded off a toothache. A string used to hang three mice could be looped around the neck with beneficial results. In case all preventive measures proved ineffective and a tooth began to ache, a man could always halt the pain by picking the offending tooth with a coffin nail, a splinter from a tree struck by lightning, the middle toe of an owl, or a needle used in making a shroud. If the tooth had to be pulled as a last resort, the sufferer looped a string around his tooth and attached it to a bent sapling. When the sapling sprang back, away flew the tooth.

The fountainhead of folk medicine on the westering frontier was the granny, who grew in reputation with each wrinkle on her face as well as each cure she effected. Elderly Dr. R. T. Whiteman of Cambridge, Idaho, found the granny still practicing in his town when he was a young physician.

"Many a granny has used a mold scraped from cheese as an application to open sores," Dr. Whiteman told me. "She got results, but she didn't know why. Today we derive penicillin from a certain type of mold. Some grannies applied wet tea leaves to a fresh burn, but modern medicine has substituted tannic acid solution, which is the active principle of tea leaves."

Grannies on the closing Idaho frontier of Dr. Whiteman's youth still inserted snuff into a woman's nose to make her sneeze and bring on labor, as they had when the frontier crossed the Alleghenies a century before. By then they had given up such old wives' practices as having the patient drink water in which nine eggs had been boiled to speed delivery.

If the baby had birthmarks, a granny counseled his parents that they could get rid of them handily. All they had to do was rub the marks with the hand of a corpse or the head of a live eel for three mornings in a row. Then they had to tie together three eel heads and hide them beneath a stone under the eaves of their house. Parents in pioneer Texas employed less morbid methods. They believed that if somebody got out of bed early and licked the baby's birthmark three times for nine successive mornings without saying a word to anyone that it would go away.

The inimitable Texan way of easing a babe through teething was to hand him a rattlesnake rattle or a six-shooter cartridge to chew on. There was some controversy as to which pacifier was the most efficacious, but most folks held that the rattlesnake rattle was best. In case a small child wet his bed, ranch mothers had a ready cure. They fed him the hind legs of a rat fried nice and crisp. This possibly pointed to a shortage of mice in pioneer Texas because during the period when the frontier crossed the Mississippi, the favorite granny cure for the unfortunate child was to regale him with field-mouse pie. Other frontiersmen of this period powdered a burned pig's bladder and spooned it into their offspring to get the desired results.

Each disease of childhood had its awesome folk remedy. To cure the croup, mother tied the right front foot of a mole around the child's neck with a blue thread. If this did not work, she took a hair from the youngster's head and hid it in a hole in an ash or oak tree. Since this was believed to prevent croup until the child had grown to the height of the hole, it was common sense to find a hole as far off the ground as possible. Whooping cough required the sufferer to be passed through a horse collar three times. Other children afflicted with this disease wore a stolen blue ribbon. Some parents reasoned that since their child had caught the disease, he ought to be able to give it away. They brought a live fish to him to catch the whooping cough and then released it in the water. It was important for somebody to observe the pond or river to see if the fish came to the surface to cough. This was a sure sign that the fish was sick, and the child would get well.

Poisonous snakes were generally in good supply on the frontier, and pioneering families were ready with cures for snake bites. Texans employed an old Indian remedy. They immediately killed the offending rattlesnake, making certain that he did not bite himself. They cut off his tail and placed the fleshy part against the bite. Mary Austin Holley, recalling the practice, says that they would then remove the snake meat and "cut off another piece of the snake, about an inch long and apply it; this is repeated until the whole snake is used up. The poison, having a greater affinity for the flesh of the serpent than for that of the man, is soon extracted."

On the frontier popular fancy had it that the best treatment for snake bite required rigorous quantities of liquor. Dr. Whiteman says that ranchers in Idaho "soaked a cloth with whiskey and wrapped it around a snake bite after slashing it open with a hunting knife." Dr. Samuel J. Crumbine reported a case in Kansas where he treated a man for snake bite while his friends, placing more faith in their own cure, plied him with drink. When he finished with the snake bite, the doctor had to treat the patient for inebriation.

Dr. Crumbine had no trouble saving his patient's life despite the mistaken assistance from his friends, but sometimes folk remedies wasted precious time. A rattlesnake struck an Oregon boy as he was walking through a grain field. His sister hurried him to a neighbor, who cut open a chicken and put his foot into the bloody insides to draw out the poison. At last they tied a tourniquet around the boy's knee and set off on horseback to see Dr. A. G. Pull, sixteen miles away in Scio. They did not reach the doctor until three hours after the bite, and the boy died.

It only seemed reasonable to frontiersmen that the rattlesnake which inflicted such serious and painful bites could help cure disease. A snakeskin was wrapped around the neck to cure a sore throat. A man shook snake rattles to rid himself of a headache; and if he was hard of hearing, he might shake the rattles and strain his ears to listen. The rattles of young snakes were considered best because they were smaller and harder to hear.

The fried heart of a rattlesnake could be eaten to cure consumption along most of the frontier as it moved westward, but Deaf Smith of Texas had a cure of his own. He claimed that the liquid ejected by an agitated skunk had supreme medicinal value. To get the benefit of the skunk, Smith killed it, removed its glands, and roasted the meat on a stick over an open fire. He claimed he cured his own consumption by living entirely on skunk meat.

Doctors find little merit in the middle-border pioneers' cure for consumption. They took a cow heel, two quarts of milk, nine ounces of hartshorn shavings, two ounces of isinglass, a quarter pound of sugar candy, and a trace of ginger and cooked the mess in an oven. If eating this meal did not cure consumption, a man could always dig a hole in the turf, climb inside it each morning, and breathe the wet ground air for fifteen minutes.

There were simples for every affliction. On the high prairies in the 1880s grannies urged that folks purify their blood with sulphur and molasses and ripen boils with bacon rind. Asafetida in a bag hung around the neck warded off contagion. A bag of asafetida or camphor around the neck also cured a cold and so did a worn stocking or a bag containing a live spider. There were various decoctions of herbs in alcohol known as bitters, which were principally given to women and children, although judging from the testimonials in the frontier newspapers, clergymen were not averse to taking a nip to calm their nerves before they inveighed against the demon rum from the pulpit. There were also secret charms to ward off illness. These were often recorded in the family Bible or passed from generation to generation. Usually the charm was given to a person of the opposite sex. If the charm failed, then the old wives would say something like, "Tansy's good for a cowboy with rheumatism, but it won't do nothing for a sheepherder."

Many pioneer families warred on disease according to the dictates of an involved system of signs and portents. Dr. Thomas McFarland of Alvin, Texas, was called to an out-of-the-way ranch where he arrived after dusk. Sick women and children were lodged inside the log ranchhouse, and men, dogs, and cats occupied the porch.

"By the powers, doctor," said the rancher, "my folks are all sick and are going to die, and I want you to go at once, and I have not got time to wait."

The doctor refused to leave but stayed with the sick through the night. In the morning he asked, "Why do you believe they are going to die?"

"The owls have been hooting and the chickens have been cackling every night for the past two weeks, and now my people are sick, and I know they are all going to die."

Dr. McFarland went out to the henhouse where he found an owl was in the roost among the chickens. The bird remained quiet until it got hungry. Then it gradually edged a hen off its perch, seized it before it hit the ground, and flew away to devour its prey. Later it returned to roost with the chickens until it was dinnertime again. The doctor reported this to the rancher, who was amazed at this light-of-day explanation for the sounds he heard at night. The doctor went on to explain that it was the drafty ranchhouse that caused all the sickness.

"Your folks'll get better if you stop the cracks between the logs and the puncheons of the floor," he said.

Ranch hands gathered moss and stuffed the cracks as the doctor directed. The cattle came around and patiently waited for the job to be finished. As soon as the men went indoors, they ate the moss out of the cracks, and the job had to be done over again. This time the rancher mounted guard with a rifle to make sure his cattle did not let the cold wind in on the family.

A man need not grow bald on the frontier. All he had to do was mix a quart of clean tar, a quart of whiskey and a quart of honey or molasses in a pewter dish and heat for twenty to thirty minutes without bringing the mess to a boil. He skimmed off the tar and bottled the brew, which was so potent that grannies claimed a tablespoonful taken three, four, or five times a day as the stomach allowed would not only put hair on a man's head, but on a woman's chest. In case the problem was simply to grow a mustache, all a middle-border youth had to do was anoint his lip with sweet cream and have a black cat lick it off at midnight.

Pioneers in Oregon checked bleeding with cobwebs. Covered-wagon women applied a poultice of wheat flour and salt for this purpose. A nosebleed on the pre-Civil War frontier called for more strenuous measures. The sufferer could chew paper, tie an eelskin to his arm, remember who sat in the next pew at the last church service or let three drops of blood fall three times on a shovel heated in the fireplace and then wipe them off.

On the middle border people bathed a wound in the head in cold cider vinegar and wrapped it in a bandage of squirrel brains and ginseng leaves. Dr. Whiteman says that Idaho old-timers "used to apply a big wad of chewing tobacco to a badly cut leg or arm." Of course, folk practitioners who believed in preventive medicine could head off a wound in the first place. All a frontiersman in the northern forests needed to do was fasten the right eye of a wolf inside his right sleeve.

As proof against mad dogs, mid-continent settlers ate bread and butter sandwiches in which they had inserted a hair of a dog. All along the frontier people carried mad stones as protection. If lockjaw developed, Dr. William Wolf of Fredericksburg, Texas, learned there was a sure folk cure. He hurried to see a youth who was foaming and in agony. The doctors told his distracted mother that he feared it was lockjaw.

"Oh, I'm so glad it is lockjaw," she replied. "I thought it was fits."

The doctor allowed that lockjaw was pretty bad, but the mother remained unworried because, as she explained, her boy would get well as soon as she gave him a good cup of cockroach tea.

Sliced onions concealed around a bedroom kept away illness. An onion in the pocket prevented smallpox. If afflicted by mumps, rub the swellings against the hog trough. Warts, as any small boy still knows, could be cured by touching them to the warty skin of a toad, but grannies assured the faithful that they would also vanish if rubbed with green walnuts, slit beans, corn, the family dishrag, bacon rind, or chicken feet. The number nine had curative powers. Nine gooseberry thorns touched to a sty would remove it in a jiffy. A snake's head and tail applied nine times to a wen dried it up, although it was considered necessary to say "amen" each time. Touch a ringworm nine times with a thimble and it would go away.

Southwestern frontiersmen used the lobelia plant both for an emetic and a purgative. Peel the plant up, and the sickness in the bowels would come up. Peel the plant down, and the sickness would go down. They chose the May apple root because its forked roots looked like a man's legs, and its stem resembled his body. The trick was to use the part of the root which matched the afflicted part.

Sometimes young frontier doctors were given a few constructive suggestions from old grannies. These varied in their usefulness. Dr. Felix Collard, Wheelock, Texas, met an old lady riding down to the forks of Camp Creek.

"Be you a doctor?" she asked.

"Yes, I'm a practicing physician."

"Do you know a sure cure for pneumonia?"

"I fear I do not."

"Well, you are a young doctor, and I want to help you along and I want to give you a sure-shot cure for pneumonia. It's black cat tail tea. Find the blackest cat that you are able to find and cut off his tail and make a tea and mix it about half and half with good red liquor and have it hot. Give one tablespoonful every ten minutes until the patient goes to sleep. The only times I've known it to fail was when the cat wasn't black enough, the tail wasn't long enough or the patient didn't get the cure soon enough."

The granny might have added that blood from the amputated tail could also cure a case of shingles.

There was a frontier notion that a headache would disappear if a man tied a rope used in a suicide or a hanging around his neck. There was no need to suffer from a fever either, because it was only necessary to eat some soup and feed the rest to a black cat to make the fever abate. More providential folks ate three hard-boiled eggs on Good Friday or held in their hand the first three hailstones of the spring to make themselves immune from fever for a whole year.

Stringent remedies were used for diseases that did not even exist. Most fearful of these imaginary illnesses was the "go-backs." A woman brought a sickly little girl to Dr. Lewis J. Moorman in Oklahoma and told him that she had the "go-backs."

"How do you know?" asked the surprised doctor.

"Because I have measured her and her body is not seven times as long as her foot. You know that is a sure sign."

She refused to let the doctor examine the girl and prepared to ride away.

"Well, I've tied a string around the buggy wheel," she said, softening a little. "If she is no better when that wears off, I will bring her back."

Other diseases were real enough, but folks living in the backwoods were understandably uncertain of their cause. Typhoid was believed by some to be caused by night air and others to be the result of putrid vegetation and animal matter in the atmosphere, grief, unripe fruit, even want of sleep and too much thinking. Dr. John Evans' and Dr. Daniel Drake's theories about cholera were unknown on the frontier except to a few educated men, and most victims of this fearful disease could only put their feet in hot ashes and water, take ten grains of calomel and one of opium and cover up in bed with hot bricks and boiled ears of corn.

Rheumatism, said granny, could be cured by carrying such oddments as a coffin nail, a potato, a horse chestnut, and a ham bone in the pocket, or a salted mackerel tied to the feet. Down in Texas Dr. George Bond of Hillsboro was treating an old lady on crutches for rheumatism, but she quit coming to see him. He met her walking on the street one day.

"What is the reason you do not come to the office?"

"I do not need to come any more. I can walk now. All my life I have heard that the sting of a bee on the heel would cure rheumatism; last week I stepped on a bee, and I am cured."

Walk around the house at midnight to alleviate asthma, cure convulsions by pouring baptismal water on a peony bush, capture a yellow toad in the neighbor's cellar and place it on the throat and quinsy will go, hang a slice of peony root on the right arm and left foot of an epileptic, and when the last piece falls off, he will be well, eat fishworms to end heartburn, throw a shovelful of hot coals over the affected parts to destroy erysipelas, boil the heart of a barn swallow in milk and wear it around the neck and the memory will clear, prevent a backache by turning a somersault when the first whippoorwill calls through the spring glades—so sounded the threnody of granny medicine through the dark forests, across the plains, the deserts, and over the high mountains to the western sea.

Chapter XIX

SADDLEBAG DRUGS AND INSTRUMENTS

A horse kicked a Klamath Falls, Oregon, ranch boy in the head and fractured his skull. Dr. John Patterson, called to the unconscious child's bedside, knew he had to relieve the pressure on his brain by removing a piece of bone, but he did not own a trephine, the cylindrical saw that surgeons use in this delicate operation. The doctor was undismayed. His frontier medical practice had accustomed him to "making do."

He took a thimble from the mother's sewing basket, sawed off the closed end, and filed teeth into the cut edge. Then he nailed the thimble to the end of a duster handle with a shingle nail. Cutting off the head of the nail, he filed it to a point so that he could center the instrument on the section of the boy's head he had to incise. Unlike many western doctors, Dr. Patterson had heard of the importance of sterilization, and he boiled his contraption in bichloride of mercury before setting to work. His patient recovered.

Frontier doctors improvised instruments and also substituted herbs for eastern drugs in an emergency. Dr. J. E. Hodge, practicing at Slim Buttes, in the Dakotas, where the nearest drugstores were 113 miles north at Belle Fourche and 200 miles east at Dickinson, often ran entirely out of pharmaceuticals.

"I had to fall back on my own resources," he recalled. "I spent many a day in the hills collecting raspberry leaves, spearmint, peppermint, and other roots and barks and herbs. I also cultivated and grew many kinds myself."

Such herbs as thyme, rue, and sweet bugle, powdered rhubarb, feverfew, fleabane, and boneset were given when the doctor could not obtain calomel, quinine, gentian, or jalap. A doctor made poultices of red pepper and mustard. He might mix up a mash of black byrony root for a mashed thumb. Sassafras oil or goose fat seemed good for most anything at least until the stagecoach came swaying into town with a new parcel of eagerly awaited medicines.

Perhaps the doctor's shipment from the East would contain cream of tartar and jalap to reduce dropsy, digitalis to control the heart's action, or santonin compounds to rout worms from intestines. The doctor might use the muriate of ammonia he found in the packet to promote expectoration, apply the nitrate of silver to the throat of a child ill of diphtheria, swab a sore with the tincture of iodine, or prepare a gargle of the chlorate of potassium. Calomel stimulated secretions, quinine combated fever, opiate stopped the bowel action, and the salts stimulated it. Sometimes western doctors were ahead of their eastern colleagues in the effective use of certain drugs. Before iodine deficiency was scientifically established as the cause of goiter, Dr. Oliver Dodson of Baker City, Oregon, used potassium iodide in treating the condition.

Since most of the drugs came in bulk form, the doctor dished them out with his pocket knife, mixed them when necessary, and packaged his prescription in a square piece of newspaper which he cut to size. He made his own tinctures and infusions with the help of horn balances and a china mortar. Dr. W. H. Hanchett, who practiced at Eugene, Oregon, was known for a hundred miles around for the show he put on as he compounded his medicines. He was a gruff, white-haired little man. Children watched with fascination as he adjusted his spectacles and opened his medical case to reveal rows of bottles. He began by lovingly running his fingers over each flask, until he found the right ones. Laying out paper squares, he sifted out the powder to the exact amount. Deftly folding the paper over, he set it aside for the patient. Dr. Hanchett also carried around a jar of jelly. When he had to give a bitter pill to a sick child, he put it in a spoonful of the jelly and shoved it in his mouth.

In the trans-Missouri West many a doctor opened his own drugstore. The rare druggist on the frontier often turned doctor, whether he had a degree or not. Sometimes the doctor and druggist owned the drugstore together. An Old West drugstore was a wonderful place of strange odors and glass carboys filled with colored liquids, of solid mahogany shelves lined with porcelain jars and rows of wooden boxes and mysterious drawers. Everything was labeled in Latin. In the rear of the store there was an iron stove. Loafers sat around it on winter nights, awaited the next chapter in life's drama, and yawned and squirted streams of tobacco juice into a box of sand provided by the druggist.

Some drugstores did a furious business; others languished. The drugstore in Calexico, California, must be included among the former, for its owner struck upon a uniquely western way to stimulate trade. When things were slow, he stepped to the door with a .22 rifle from which he had removed the sights. He would toss a bunch of nickles in the air and begin shooting. This deadeye pharmacist is never known to have missed a coin. A crowd always gathered to see him shoot. At the end of the show folks trooped inside to do their buying.

Most mining camps and cow towns came to have drugstores, but even then a doctor who rode a long distance to see a patient often had to rely upon the contents of his saddlebags to make his cures. These saddlebags were never a thing of beauty, according to Dr. Francis A. Long, a Nebraska prairie doctor of the 1880s, but they were a beautiful sight to the afflicted. The bags were actually two leather pouches fitted with compartments for the physician's bottles and connected by a heavy, broad leather strap two feet or more long which fitted across the saddle. In them the doctor carried powders, liquids, and hand-rolled pills. The bags also might contain the doctor's lance, cutting knife, forceps, lint, ligatures, sponge, bandages, plasters, catheter, a stomach pump, a syringe, splints, caustics, a heating iron, sutures, and a tourniquet.

Galloping up to a lonely ranch or cabin, the doctor swung down off his horse and carried his saddle bags to the side of his patient. He routinely took temperatures, counted the pulse, looked at the tongue and the skin, and considered the general appearance. He asked how the sufferer felt, where he hurt, questioned him about his appetite, bowel movements, and changes in weight. From this superficial diagnosis he had to determine the disease and arrive at a course of treatment.

With no miracle drugs to help him, a saddlebag doctor often improvised cures. Some applied poultices of flaxseed or corn meal to the side to cure lobar pneumonia and placed their patients in a quilted pneumonia jacket to keep them warm. Dr. William Pruden in Oregon's John Day Valley applied steaming hot towels to the chest of a boy choking with the disease. The parents demanded that he quit, but he continued his rigorous treatment, even augmenting it with glasses of hot water until at last the child breathed easily and recovered.

Dr. Theophilus Degen in Oregon said, "There is life in heat and death in cold."

He had the family heat rocks in the fireplace, wrap them in cloths, and place them in the patient's bed. He made his own medicines as a matter of course, and relied heavily on red pepper and mustard poultices and herb teas. He also fashioned an inhalation apparatus out of an earthen churn and an elderberry limb. By forcing the pitch out of the limb, he made a tube through which a person suffering from chest congestion could breathe inhalants from hot vinegar poured over herbs in the churn.

The clinical thermometer was introduced in the East in the 1850s and soon afterward reached the Far West. Not all frontier doctors accepted the thermometer. To many of them it was enough to place a practiced hand on a sick man's brow and learn that he had a fever. What did it matter exactly how high the temperature was?

In 1879 Dr. Isaac W. Starr, a young doctor starting his practice at Brownsville, Oregon, was called into consultation on a puzzling fever case by Dr. Robert H. Crawford, a gray-haired veteran, who had crossed the plains in '53. Dr. Starr took out his thermometer and prepared to put it in the patient's mouth. With an impatient sweep of his hand Dr. Crawford brushed it aside. He did not use the newfangled thing, he explained.

"I don't need it. I get along all right without it," he said.

Early frontier doctors as a rule had little notion of the importance of sterilizing their hands and instruments before surgery. They washed their instruments in warm water only to remove the dust. Dr. Francis Long said:

"It was suggested that one should wash his hands with soap and water before making an examination or any obstetric procedure and should lubricate the examining hand with soap, unsalted lard or vaseline. We were told the forceps before using should be immersed in warm water and lubricated. . . . I do not recall that any suggestion was made of any surgical cleansing of the patient."

Pioneer Kansas doctors wore street clothes under aprons encrusted with dried blood as they performed an operation. Their surgical needles and the catgut to be used for sutures dangled from their coat lapels or were kept in their coat pockets. A doctor washed his hands after the operation but not before. Sponges used to sop up the blood and pus were rinsed out and considered ready to use again.

On the other hand, some western doctors very early developed firm ideas as to the importance of sterilization. F. A. Bailey in the Oregon Territory of the 1870s baked his homemade dressings in the kitchen oven before applying them to a wound. He boiled his instruments in the family wash boiler. As the years went by, Lister's technique spread along the frontier. In 1869 Dr. S. T. Odell of St. Louis, Kansas, used carbolic acid as an antiseptic on a compound fracture. California mining-camp doctors were using carbolic acid by 1871, yet for decades afterward, many doctors preferred whiskey as an antiseptic and in remote Montana sheep camps, Dr. R. P. R. Gordon used turpentine.

Rubber gloves became popular with surgeons in the East, and here and there a western doctor treasured a pair. When Dr. Fred Peterson arrived at Calexico, California, his predecessor proudly took him into his office.

"Let me show you how to preserve rubber gloves here," he said. "This terrific heat very quickly takes all the life out of rubber, unless it is specially cared for. I find that by keeping them immersed in a covered jar of white ammonia they keep well."

Tenderly the doctor took his precious gloves from a two-quart glass container. Mysteriously, they had expanded to four times their original size and all their elasticity was gone. The desert doctors had no choice but to do their surgery with bare hands.

Right up to the closing of the frontier in 1893 whiskey continued to be preferred to chloroform as an anesthetic by both patients and doctors. Doctors operated in an emergency without benefit of either one. Then the surgeon's tableside manner became critical. If his wrist trembled as he prepared to cut, the patient screamed in agony even before he felt the bite of the knife. Many doctors, and notably Ephraim McDowell, essayed the gentle, soothing approach to surgery without anesthetics. Others bullied their patients into submission. Ephraim McDowell's nephew, Dr. Joseph Nashe McDowell, was among these. He cherished a rich store of purple language. When he was called to amputate the leg of a man crushed in a sawmill, he came raging through the door.

"Where is the damn rascal?" he roared. "I have come to cut him to pieces, damn his trifling soul! Why did he not keep away from the damned machinery?"

Catching sight of the pain-wracked man, he shouted. "Sir, I have come to cut you up, damn you! The instruments are all ready." He waved the knife before the man's frightened eyes. "Now, sir, hold still and I will make quick work of it."

He cut off the limb and dressed the wound. Then he asked his patient how he felt.

"Doctor, you frightened me so badly I did not feel you cut my leg off."

"My poor unfortunate," gently said the surgeon. "I felt all your pain for you." He apologized for his savage behavior.

Obstetrics by a tallow candle or kerosene lamp, the amputation of frozen fingers and toes with the aid of soap, hot water, and mercuric bichloride solution, extraction of a grain of corn from a small girl's trachea with the assistance of two hairpins fastened to twigs, removal of a twenty-five-cent piece from the esophagus of a twelve-year-old boy with a turkey quill—frontier doctors were astonishingly successful. Dr. C. D. Ball, reflecting upon early surgery in Orange County, California, summed up:

"Without the aid of hospitals and white linen nurses, poorly equipped with instruments on the kitchen table, they operated the strangulated hernia, amputated legs and arms, trephined the skull, resected bones, straightened club feet, corrected hair lips and the like. They even invaded the abdomen, suturing gunshot and knife wounds of the intestines."

Dr. Urling Coe contrived to make a woman's delivery easier. He described his apparatus as follows:

"In some of these cases I was obliged to make a forceps delivery alone. I had a special harness constructed, my own invention, for use in such cases. It had rather large cuffs to go around the thighs with an adjustable metal bar between them to hold the thighs wide apart. From the cuffs a leather strap ran up over the shoulders, held knees to chest."

The doctor packed a large wad of cotton in the bottom of an ordinary drinking glass so tightly that it would not fall out when the glass was turned upside down. The cotton was saturated with chloroform.

"The patient was then told to hold the inverted glass over her nose," he said, "and inhale regularly and fairly deeply. When she had taken enough chloroform to make her insensible to pain and put her to sleep, her hand relaxed and she dropped the glass before she took too much."

As the frontier crossed the Mississippi, bloodletting was still a standard medical practice. A few early western doctors bled so many patients that they constructed troughs to carry the blood out of their offices.

"Bleed her to death," old Dr. John Bernhisel advised young Dr. W. F. Anderson at Salt Lake City in the 1850s. He actually meant, "Bleed her until she faints."

In Texas Dr. Martin Read was an equally ardent bleeder. He used a scarifier. When the gadget's spring was pressed down, it forced tiny knives through the patient's skin. The doctor then drew blood with a wet cupping glass. By the 1870s bloodletting was rare even in the most remote parts of the West. Dr. W. J. Burge of Atchison, Kansas, wrote with satisfaction, "The lancet has finished its course and been laid away in the grave as quietly as many of its former victims."

A doctor's office was usually in his home. In it he might have a wood and leather operating chair, a cabinet cluttered with his instruments and bottles of drugs. There often was a skeleton or at least a colorfully lithographed chart of the human body, which served the purpose of entertaining patients as they waited for the doctor to return from a call.

Sometimes the doctor had a crude laboratory in his office. Dr. Will Mayo in Minnesota made routine urinalyses. He boiled a teaspoon of the fluid over a candle or lamp and then tested it for sugar with a few drops of Fehling's solution. He also was able to isolate albumen in the urine.

Much of the doctor's equipment was homemade. Dr. A. E. Spahn of Corpus Christi, Texas, in 1876 improvised a tourniquet which served so well it was adapted as a field instrument by the U. S. Army. At Virginia City, Montana, Dr. Ira C. Smith also had an inventive turn of mind. When the telegraph line reached Montana in 1866, he studied the receiving and sending equipment. Finally he took a receiver and from it made a device which he attached to his patient's arm. The pulsations of the blood were picked up and transmitted to another receiver which guided a stylus in drawing a pulse pattern on a piece of paper blackened over a lamp chimney. He successfully used his invention long before the cardiograph came into use.

Dr. Smith also built ingenuous supports for broken legs, which he elevated by pulleys and strings. When he could not set a broken leg, he nailed the bones together with small nails. For skeletal traction in fractures of the femur pioneer doctor, C. A. Robins, told me that in the Idaho lumber camps doctors had the lumberjack blacksmith forge a pair of tongs. Splints could always be torn from a pigpen or a house or shed siding and shaped with a jackknife. In the Southwest Dr. Henry Hoyt made his splints out of adobe mud when he could not obtain plaster of Paris.

Doctors improvised equipment for dentistry. In the Oregon bunch-grass country, Dr. Urling C. Coe regularly functioned at "tooth-pulling bees." Cowboys with toothaches rode to the host ranch from all over the range. Whiskey flasks passed from hand to hand; everybody drank and sang. Out in the yard Dr. Coe placed two kitchen chairs next to one another. His patient sat in one chair while the roistering gang crowded close. Putting his left foot on the seat of the other chair, Coe had his patient lay his head on his knee. Quickly he encircled the man's head with his left arm in a strangle hold and seized his lower jaw with his left hand. Wielding the forceps in his right hand, he grappled with the decayed tooth and pulled it out by brute strength. Dr. Coe would pull out thirty to forty teeth at a session. It was a tough experience, agreed the cowboys, but not nearly so tough as having a blacksmith knock an aching tooth out with a punch and hammer.

When pharmaceutical companies began to ship their drugs to the West in glass bottles, many a frontier doctor looked suspiciously at this innovation. Patients were equally suspicious of bottles. Dr. William Wallace, Schulenburg, Texas, gave several small bottles of calomel to the wife of a German settler. He was sitting on his porch one day when the German galloped up on his plow horse, which was still in field harness.

"Mine Gott in Himmel, Doctor, come quick," cried the German, "Mine wife she swallowed dem little glass pottles unt dey are cutting her pelly to pieces."

The doctor rode twelve miles to the settler's farm to prove to him that it was just the calomel griping his wife. Still another settler emptied out the capsules that the doctor had given him and brought them back for a refund. Another Texas doctor in the Brazos Bottom fared little better with a new medicine, which was bitter. Dr. Robert Harris asked the mother of a sick boy to whom he had given the medicine whether the child had taken it all.

"Po' little feller, it was so bitter he could not take it, Doc," she replied.

The mother had thoughtfully taken the medicine for her poor "little feller."

"Making do" with the drugs and instruments at hand, doctors among the ranches, logging camps, mining towns and isolated settlements of the West, succored the sick and injured as best they could and hoped for the day when more settled conditions and better transportation would provide them with the full arsenal of the medical pharmacopoeia.

Chapter XX

INQUIRING MINDS

Mary Maverick of the pioneer San Antonio family which later gave Texas a succession of prominent politicians was visiting a woman friend on March 19, 1840, the day of the big Indian fight outside of town. The settlers won the fight; the ladies, seated at a grated window at the front of the house, were chatting about it over a reassuring cup of tea.

Mary saw Dr. Weideman dismount in the dusty street. In the battle he not only had sutured wounds but had shouldered a rifle. Now he strolled over to the window where the ladies were sitting.

"With your permission, Madam," he said.

He put a severed Indian head on the window sill. Bowing courteously, he sauntered over to his horse and returned with still another head, which he placed beside the first. The tea in the ladies' cups lost its flavor; their conversation ceased. Next the doctor lugged up two whole bodies. He smiled politely at the wide-eyed women.

"I have been longing exceedingly to secure such specimens, and now, ladies, I must get a cart to take them home," he said.

The doctor hurried away. The ladies were left to survey his grisly prizes and to wonder in horror how the kind old doctor, who tenderly cared for the sick and was known to weep in frustration at being unable to alleviate a child's earache, could be acting so strangely. They could hardly know that the scientist that lurks within all good doctors had come to the surface in Dr. Weideman.

That night in his kitchen the doctor put the bodies and heads in a huge soap boiler, added water and stewed them over a hot flame to loosen the flesh. Long before dawn he emptied the gruesome broth into the waters of the nearby Acequia Ditch and contentedly put the skeletons away to dry. Alas, in his scientific zeal, Dr. Weideman had forgotten one thing. Early-nineteenth-century San Antonio citizens bathed and laundered in the river, but the clear waters of the Acequia were used only for drinking.

By the morning of the twenty-first, San Antonians were up in arms. They came to the belated conclusion that for an entire day and night they had been swallowing bits of Indian with every drink of water. Women shrieked; men vomited. Some pregnant mothers even aborted. A crowd of angry men marched on the doctor, arrested him, and brought him to trial.

In the courtroom Dr. Weideman was astounded at the havoc he had caused. Why, nobody's been drinking Indian soup, he assured the judge. The Indians had washed on down the ditch the first night. Didn't San Antonio believe in science?

No, San Antonio did not believe in science. At least the judge gave the doctor a heavy fine, and everybody in town assured him bluntly that if it were not for his previous life as a good Samaritan that he would have been run out of town at the business end of a six-shooter.

"Look, Doc," people said, "can't you just stick to curing folks and leave this science business alone?"

The doctor promised to refrain from emptying Indian stew into the Acequia, but he staunchly maintained that a doctor by nature and training was a scientist; and even if he practiced on the benighted frontier, he must make his contributions to medical research.

An impressive number of doctors on the westering American frontier from the Alleghenies to the Pacific Ocean would have agreed with Dr. Weideman. Civilian doctors as well as military surgeons probed medical frontiers even as they fought disease on the geographical frontier, and they did this from the earliest days of the westward trek. The first professor of medicine in the English colonies was Dr. John Morgan. In 1765 he considered the vast stretches of wilderness, of forest and mountain and plains and asked, "How many plants are there, natives of this soil, possessed of peculiar virtues? How many fossils to enrich the cabinets of the curious? How many natural substances, objects of new trade and commerce to supply materials for various arts, as well as to enlarge the bounds of medicine?"

Nor did Anglo-American doctors alone possess a scientist's inquiring mind. In 1785 a French expedition under the command of Count Jean François Galaup de La Pérouse anchored for ten days at Monterey, California. Five doctors, imbued with the philosophy of Voltaire, went ashore to answer the question, "Are dislocations, fractures, hernias and surgical diseases in general very common among men living in a state of Nature?" The doctors also wanted to learn if "men are frequently found in America whose breasts afford milk in sufficient quantity to suckle children."

Chief Surgeon Rollin found that Monterey Indians were larger than those of Chile, smaller than those of Alaska, more stupid than those of either country. They suffered from pulmonary disorders because of the damp climate, experienced dysentery, rheumatism, epilepsy, the itch, and ophthalmia. They tattooed themselves and poisoned their arrows. The tattoos were harmless, and the poison was largely ineffectual. No man consented to produce any milk at all for the sake of science.

Many of the doctors on the frontier were adventurous young men from the best medical schools in Europe and America. With a doctor's natural interest in the medicinal properties of plants, they botanized with energy. Archibald Menzies, an English naval surgeon, who accompanied Captain George Vancouver's exploration of what is now the Washington coast in 1792, frequently went ashore to study plants and animals. He brought back specimens to London's Kew Gardens. On the Russian Kotzebue expedition in 1816, Dr. Johann Frederick Eschscholtz was the physician. He too studied the flora of the coast, and the scientific name of the California poppy is Eschscholtzia Californica. Later Dr. William Tolmie of the Hudson's Bay Company continued the botanical exploration of the Pacific coast. Searching for medical herbs, he made the first ascent of Mount Rainier. He described the mountain-top glaciers which "spangled and sparkled brightly in the bright sunshine," and collected valuable plants, some of which he kept for the preparation of medicines. He sent others home to England.

Dr. Tolmie had a romantic bent. He met an Indian princess, "noted on both sides of the mountain for her personal charms and powerfully fascinating manner, no person within the sphere of her attraction being capable of resisting. She is the best looking native I have seen. About middle-sized, a dark brunette with a large, dark languishing eye, pearly teeth and finely formed limbs, and there is native grace in all her actions. She is now wedded to a petty portage chief, who, jealous as Otheloe, bangs her frequently with a paddle or the butt end of a musket."

Another Hudson's Bay surgeon, John Scoulder, studied plants and animals in 1825 and also made a medical record of native diseases. He noted a case of intestinal obstruction and much apoplexy, smallpox, enteritis, gonorrhea, and syphilis among the Indians. Becoming interested in the curious Chinook custom of flattening the skulls of children, he dug into an Indian burial place. He had unearthed three splendid specimens when tribesmen surprised him. He fled for his life to a British ship in the harbor.

Still a later Hudson's Bay surgeon, Dr. Forbes Barclay, studied the virulence of the great 1844 epidemic of dysentery. He reported that by 1849 the disease had become milder but was by then endemic in the country. In 1847 American settlers brought measles over the Oregon Trail to the Pacific Northwest. He observed the severity with which the disease raged among the Indians and how it in turn became milder as the native population developed a partial immunity to it.

Anglo-American doctors who advanced into the wilderness with the settlers were as keen in their scientific pursuits as were the Hudson's Bay Company's surgeons. Dr. John Lambert Richmond made medical history in an unfloored and unchinked cabin on the Ohio River frontier.

Richmond was a farm boy who became the janitor at the Medical College of Ohio, where the greatest of the American frontier medical scientists, Dr. Daniel Drake, helped him to study medicine and to earn his degree. Richmond was also a Baptist minister, and he was preaching an evening sermon at Newtown near Cincinnati when he heard that a woman across the flooding Little Miami River had been in labor for thirty hours and was about to die after repeated convulsions. The doctor-minister rowed a skiff across the river's rushing waters to find an enormous Negro woman with a deformed pelvis, which prevented a normal delivery.

The night was stormy; the wind howled through the log walls and kept blowing the doctor's candle out. Friends had to screen the flickering flames with blankets as the doctor made an incision in the dying woman's abdomen. With only his pocket case of instruments, Dr. Richmond performed the first Caesarean section in the United States. Within five weeks his patient had fully recovered.

Other frontier surgeons also advanced surgical techniques. Dr. Robert Calvin Coffey of Colfax, Oregon, operated upon young pigs with bowel protrusions and developed the method of replacing the uterus that bears his name. Dr. Andrew Fabrique of Wichita, Kansas, experimented with skin grafts on dogs. He became adept at opening skulls in accident cases and operated successfully for brain abscesses. He was the first western surgeon to open the common duct for gallstones.

Many doctors had their homemade laboratories in which they could feel they were blood brother to the great men of medical science in Europe and the East. Dr. T. C. Osborn, Cleburne, Texas, had such a laboratory. For sixty years he rode out to make his medical rounds. At night he studied malaria in his lab. He never succeeded in fathoming malaria, but he discovered the use of bichloride of mercury solution in the treatment of smallpox rash.

Frontier doctors considered the effects of whiskey on their hard-drinking patients and made observations on the weather and the incidence of goiters. Dr. James Simpson of Grass Valley, California, inquired into the toxicity of dynamite fumes in the mines. Tall, thin Dr. James Blake arrived at Middletown in the California gold fields in 1849. At this early date he studied the correlation of atomic weight and the valences of metals as well as their pharmacological action.

Doctors were frequently agricultural pioneers. Dr. George A. Kenny determined to raise apples on his ranch seventeen miles from Salmon, Idaho. Cowboys laughed. Everybody knew that the country was too high and cold for apples, everybody but Dr. Kenny who sent east for Siberian crab-apple trees. He raised wagonloads of apples and made a tangy cider which was popular at ranch parties. His apple trees are still bearing. Dr. Kenny also started a dairy, and when his cows produced a surplus of butter, he put it up in tin cans.

"Doc thinks you can preserve butter like beans," folks said.

That winter when cream production almost ceased, he opened up his tins and sold fresh butter at the trading post at Salmon.

Dr. Guillermo B. Osbourn brought roses, vines, and fruit trees from Rochester, New York, to Southern California in 1855. Soon he was shipping grapes to the East. Twenty years later Dr. John L. Dryer of Coloma made a more significant contribution to California's future as the nation's fruit bowl. He was the first to smudge a citrus grove to head off frost damage.

Frontiersmen smiled at the doctor's laboratory, his studious ways, his predilection for plants, animals, Indians, and such incomprehensible things as the atomic weights of metals, but when he took to studying the dead so that the living might be benefited, he was quickly labeled a "vulture of the scalpel." Tough miners gagged when Dr. Charles Cole of Helena, Montana, exhumed the body of Con Murphy, a bandit, who was hanged on a railroad trestle east of town. Even at that Murphy's cadaver made out rather well in comparision with that of Big Nose George, a desperado who bushwhacked the sheriff of a Wyoming made out rather well in comparison with that of Big Nose boarded a train and rode as far as Helena, where a posse yanked him to the station platform and summarily strung him up.

A doctor procured the body and pickled it in a barrel. Unfortunately, he forgot about poor Big Nose. Years later, with the doctor's death, neighbors opened up the barrel and there was George!

With a Westerner's sense of the proprieties, folks contributed to a fund to send George back to Wyoming where he was buried in the graveyard near the sheriff he had murdered.

When Dad Bender of the notorious outlaw family murdered a youth on an Idaho trail and stole his horse and saddle, Sheriff John Snook of Salmon pursued him into Montana. He hog-tied the badman and returned him to Salmon, where he chained him in the cellar for safekeeping. That night Bender sawed at his leg in an effort to escape his bonds and bled to death. Dr. George Kenny took time off from worrying about his fledgling apple trees to claim the body. Back at his ranch, he boiled the corpse in the hog-butchering vat and then placed it atop a shed so that the magpies could pick it clean. In time he sent the skull to an eastern laboratory where it was pronounced a "criminal type." In Lemhi County, Idaho, they say that the skull was sent back west but never reached the doctor. Instead Dad Bender's bony visage was used for years as a decoration on a freight-wagon brake pole.

Dr. Kenny's anatomical bent also got him into trouble with the Indians. He wanted a skeleton so that he could study bone structures. Going to an Indian burial ground, he discovered a mummified head. This he brought home and cooked in a huge kettle on his kitchen stove. Unfortunately, two squaws came into the kitchen to beg a morsel of food, lifted the pot lid, and drew back in horror. It was years before the tribe would believe that Dr. Kenny was not eating Indians, heads and all.

Even the brilliant Dr. Joseph Nashe McDowell, nephew of Ephraim McDowell, was sought by a lynching mob for robbing a grave. Dr. McDowell, who had married the sister of his teacher, Daniel Drake, practiced surgery from the Alleghenies to the Rockies from 1840 to 1860. He also taught anatomy at Ohio College, and, needing a body for demonstration purposes, he paid a midnight visit to a graveyard and dug up a recently dead girl. He had scarcely left the cemetery when her friends and relatives discovered that the body had been stolen. They hurried to the college building and rode around it, firing off their guns and waving a sturdy rope.

McDowell was trapped in the building. As the mob smashed in the door, he hid the body in the attic and then raced down the stairs to the second-floor dissecting room. Heavy boots thundered up the stairs. Quickly the doctor climbed on a slab and pulled a shroud over his body. Shouting men burst into the room.

"Here is a fellow who died with his boots on," cried one, rapping McDowell's feet. "I guess he's a fresh one."

They could not find the corpse they wanted, nor could they find the doctor.

One doctor even lived in fear of the vengeance of Jesse James as a result of his yen for a skeleton. When the James gang made its ill-starred raid on Northfield, Minnesota, on September 7, 1876, bandit Charley Pitts was shot down in the street. Henry F. Hoyt, home from medical school at Rush Medical College in Chicago, was given the body. He decided to preserve the skeleton for later use in his office.

To bleach the bones Hoyt packed them in a box and lowered it into the south branch of Lake Como outside of St. Paul. Upon graduation from medical school, he set off into the West on a career which took him from Deadwood to Texas and on into New Mexico, where he became a friend of Billy the Kid. He forgot all about the skeleton bleaching in the waters of Lake Como.

Years later a youth hunting muskrats with a spear and a hatchet crossed the lake on the winter ice and saw the box. Chopping through the ice, he knocked off the end of the box. It was full of bones. These must be bones set aside for a dog, he figured. His father thought otherwise. Cutting into the ice, he knocked off the end of the box. Out rolled a skull! The sheriff and coroner hurried to the lake. Bullet holes in the bones spoke of murder.

Newspapers throughout the country ran stories of the grisly find in Lake Como, and the sheriff hunted for clues and motives to no avail. Then somebody remembered Dr. Hoyt and his desire for a skeleton. The crime was solved, and newspapers across the nation reported the solution. Soon Dr. Hoyt received a letter, which bitterly complained of his treatment of "pore Charley pitts."

"I'll get yu yit," concluded the writer, who did not sign his name. The doctor was sure it was Jesse James.

Hot Springs is six miles from Las Vegas, New Mexico. From time to time Dr. Hoyt dined in an adobe inn at the springs with Billy the Kid Bonney. The doctor considered his lethal young friend a fascinating psychological study. One day as they were enjoying a meal, a bleak-eyed man joined them. The Kid said he was a friend from Missouri—a "Mr. Howard." As they ate, the doctor noticed that the Kid's friend was missing the tip of a finger on his left hand. It was Jesse James! But if he recognized his luncheon companion as the man who had treated "pore Charley pitts" so very poorly, he made no sign and rode away from the inn as peacefully as he had come.

The years passed and the frontier was changing. Even Dr. Weideman's San Antonio was becoming educated not only to scientific ways but to scientific jargon. In 1882 a ranch-country scribe summed up what he felt about the new look to medicine in the city of the Alamo. In his home town people still died of simple frontier diseases such as lead poisoning, but in San Antonio, well now! Science was running rampant.

"Over in San Antonio," he observed, "the people died of icterus senilis, of seven kinds of tuberculoses, of icterus amenorrhoea, intestinalis pulmonalis, and five other kinds of icterus. They can also die, if they want to, of anenisina, colica flatulenta biliosa—particularly when complicated with atropia medullae spinalis or morasmus infantium caused probably by too much vox populi, nux vomica, e pluribus unum, etc., particularly etc."

Doctors of the West proved as immune to jests and satire as they earlier had been to threats and mob violence. They continued to pursue the grail of medical science. Out of necessity they were an independent breed, both self-reliant and creative in their medical practices. Out of their isolated practices grew a spirit of inquiry which led them to explore the frontiers of science even as they helped to push back the frontiers of America. How valuable were their studies of epidemics, anatomy, surgical techniques, skin grafts, alcoholism, mine conditions, and all the other things which intrigued their restless minds? What use were their investigations of botany, ornithology, anthropology, and agriculture? Dr. William H. Welch, first Dean of Johns Hopkins Medical School, was in a position to judge their scientific work.

"The best of these men were, withal, abreast in knowledge, training and skill with their contemporaries of the Atlantic coast," he said. "They were men of striking originality, substantial contributors to the sum of medical knowledge and art, powerful influences in the material, as well as the medical development of the Far West."

BIBLIOGRAPHY

1. MANUSCRIPTS, LETTERS, AND DOCUMENTS

American Medical Association Historical Committee. "Milestones in the History of Medicine in the Pacific Northwest," Clinical Session, Seattle, Washington, November 27–30, 1956.

Brougher, John C., M.D., Vancouver, Washington. Manuscript, "Early Medicine in the Pacific Northwest."

Charnock, Donald A., M.D. "Medicine Moves West," paper read before the 55th Annual Meeting of the Medical Library Association at Los Angeles, California, June 18–22, 1956.

Courier, log. Entry of Thursday, 9th. March, 1825, to be found at the National Library of Medicine, Bethesda, Md.

Courville, Cyril B., M.D. "Observations on Cranial Injuries on the Western Frontier," paper read before the 55th Annual Meeting of the Medical Library Association at Los Angeles, California, June 18–22, 1956.

Delp, Mahlon, M.D. Manuscript, "The Gunfighters' Surgeon."

Department of the Army, Office of the Surgeon General, Technical Liaison Office, Washington, D.C. Document, "Army Medical Service Celebrates 185th Anniversary on 27 July, 1960."

De Wolf, James, M.D. Typewritten copy of his letters written in the campaign preceding the Battle of the Little Big Horn in 1876. Contained in the Ayer Collection, the Newberry Library, Chicago, Ill.

Divine, Robert M., Foreman of CY Ranch, Forks of Caspar, Wyoming. The original ranch log book is at the Newberry Library, Chicago, Ill.

Ertell, Charles H., Jr., Captain, M.S.C., Chief, Technical Liaison Division. Letter to Kenneth N. Anderson, Editor, *Today's Health*, American Medical Association, dated February 20, 1963.

E. S. C., Dr. Letter from San Francisco to his former colleagues in Chicago, dated January 13, 1869, at National Library of Medicine, Bethesda, Md.

Estes, J. Worth, Boston University School of Medicine, Boston,

Mass. Letters to author and a "Tabulation of Ephraim McDowell's Ovariectomies."

Headquarters, Fifth U. S. Army, Chicago, Illinois. "Fact Sheet" of July 1962, "First to Win Army Medal of Honor."

McDowell, Ephraim, M.D. Letter to Robert Thompson, Philadelphia, Pa., written at Danville, Ky., January 2, 1829.

Proceedings of the Convention for the Organization of the Nebraska State Medical Society, June 24, 1868, Omaha, Nebraska.

Reports on Operations of the U. S. Marine Hospital Service, Washington, D.C., 1897.

Robins, C. A., M.D., Lewiston, Idaho. Letters and notes sent to author.

Russell, Don, Sheriff, the Westerners, Chicago Corral. Letters and conversations with the author.

Schlicke, C. P., M.D., Spokane, Wash. Manuscript, "Concerning Some 18th. Century Physicians in the Pacific Northwest."

Whiteman, R. T., M.D., Cambridge, Idaho. Correspondence with author concerning his early medical practice in Idaho.

Whitwell, Nora W. Manuscript prepared for author, "Early History of Dr. Whitwell's Life in Lemhi County, Idaho," and other notes concerning the doctor's life.

Wilkins, Marcia W., Bethesda, Md. Letter of February 28, 1962, to author.

Woodworth, John. "Cholera Epidemic of 1873," House Executive Document 95 of the 43rd. Congress, 2nd. session.

Wyman, W. "Hygiene of Steamboats on the Western Rivers," pages 193–205 of the Report, Supervising Surgeon, General Marine Hospital, 1882.

Ybarguen, Frank Wright. Letter of February 12, 1962, to Louise Shadduck of the State of Idaho's Department of Commerce and Development, Boise, Idaho, concerning his grandfather, Dr. Frank S. Wright of Lemhi, Idaho.

2. PERIODICALS

Adams, V. K., M.D. "The Medical Pioneers," *New Mexico Magazine*, May 1950.

Airey, J. D., M.D. "The Effects of Railroads on Climatic Diseases in the South and West," *St. Louis Medical and Surgical Journal*, V. 9, pages 717–24, 1872.

Andrews, E. "Military Surgery among the Apaches," *Chicago Medical Examiner*, V. 10, pages 599–601, 1869.

Babcock, J. M. "The History of Medicine in Oklahoma," *Journal of the Oklahoma Medical Association*, V. 46, page 216, August 1953.

Barnes, Frank L. "Some of the Duties of the Local Surgeon," *Texas State Journal of Medicine*, V. 22, 1906–7.

Beaumont, William. "A Case of Wounded Stomach," *Medical Recorder*, V. 8, pages 14–19, 1825. Erroneously attributed to Surgeon General Joseph Lovell, who submitted the manuscript on behalf of Surgeon Beaumont.

Beaumont, William. "Further Experiments on the Case of Alexis San Martin Who Was Wounded in the Stomach by a Load of Duck Shot," *Medical Recorder*, V. 9, pages 94–97, 1826.

Beyer, Theodore E., M.D. "The Gold Rush—Its Cost in Health and Life," *Rocky Mountain Medical Journal*, V. 56, No. 5, May 1959.

Blount, Daniel M., M.D. "Observations on Railway Travel," *St. Louis Medical and Surgical Journal*, pages 26–30, 1890.

Brougher, John C., M.D. "Pioneer Medicine in Clarke County, Washington," *Northwest Medicine*, V. 57, pages 739–46, June 1958.

Cope, Zachary. "Pioneer Physician," *British Medical Journal*, No. 5270, page 47, January 6, 1962.

Craven, J. T., M.D. "Railroad Surgery," *Transactions of the Colorado Medical Society*, pages 98–104, 1881, Denver, Colo.

Crumbine, Samuel J., M.D. "Were the Old Days Really Good," *Today's Health*, V. 32, No. 8, August 1954.

Dawler, B. "Musings on Railroad Travel from a Hygienic Point of View," *New Orleans Medical and Surgical Journal*, V. 17, pages 598–603, 1860.

"Dengue at Dallas," "Progress," writing in *Southern California Practitioner*, V. 2, 1887.

De Voto, Bernard. "Frontier Family Medicine," *What's New*, V. 192, pages 3–5, 1955.

Dunne, Roy. "A Post with a Past—and a Future, *The Westerners Brand Book*, Chicago Corral, V. 19, No. 11, January 1963.

Everhard, Ola. "They Knew What to Do," *Frontier Times*, V. 36, No. 2, Spring 1962.

Ewing, W. T., M.D. "On Mountain Fever," *St. Louis Medical and Surgical Journal*, 1855.

Frazier, J. M. "Evolution in Study and Practice of Medicine in 60 Years in Texas," *Texas State Medical Journal*, V. 32, pages 300–5.

French, H. E. "Medicine in North Dakota—70 Year Span," *Journal-Lancet*, V. 71, pages 2–8, January 1951.

Frost, Woodhull, "Ranch Remedies in Man, Bird and Beast," *Texas Folklore Society Publication*, V. 8, 1930.

"A Gallery of Governors," *Pfizer Spectrum*, V. 6, No. 21, December 1, 1958.

Gemmel, Belle A., M.D. "Utah Medical History: Some Reminiscences," *California and Western Medicine*, V. 36, No. 1, January 1932.

Goodfellow, George E., M.D. "Cases of Gunshot Wound of the Abdomen Treated by Operation," *Southern California Practitioner*, V. 4, pages 209–17, 1889.

Goodfellow, George E., M.D. "Case of Sudden Death in Thoracentesis," *Medical Record*, V. 16, page 476, 1879.

Goodfellow, George E., M.D. "The Gila Monster Again," *Scientific American*, V. 96, page 371, 1907.

Goodfellow, George E., M.D. "Note on the Impenetrability of Silk to Bullets," *Southern California Practitioner*, V. 2, pages 95–98, 1887.

Gray, John S. "Will Comstock—the Natty Bumppo of Kansas," *The Westerners Brand Book*, Chicago Corral, V. 18, No. 12, February 1962.

Grinnell, F. "The Healing Art," *Cincinnati Lancet and Observer*, V. 17, pages 145–47, 1874.

Groh, George. "Doctors of the Frontier," *American Heritage*, V. 14, No. 3, April 1963.

Harvey, P. F. "The Climate and Diseases of Northern Dakota and Montana," *Medical Review*, V. 15, pages 343–46, 1879.

Horine, Emmet Field, M.D. "The Stage Setting for Ephraim McDowell, 1771–1830," *Bulletin of the History of Medicine*, V. 24, page 149, 1950.

Horner, G. R. B., M.D. "On the Diseases and Injuries of Seamen," *The Medical Examiner*, August 18, 1853.

Ivey, Thomas N., M.D. "Medicine in the Pioneer West (1850–1900)," *The New Physician*, V. 9, No. 9, September, 1960.

"Jayhaw Medicine," *Journal of the American Medical Association*, V. 175, No. 12, March 25, 1961.

Johnson, Murray L., M.D. "Early Medical Men in the Northwest Who Were Naturalists," *Journal of the American Medical Association*, V. 175, No. 8, October 29, 1960.

Kurtz, Joseph, M.D. "Notes on Railroad Injuries," *Southern California Practitioner*, V. 2, pages 102–8, 1887.

Larsell, O. "Medical History in the Northwest," *Bulletin of the Medical Library Association,* V. 29, pages 73–80, December 1940.

Lathrop, Amy. "Pioneer Remedies from Western Kansas," *Western Folklore,* V. 20, No. 1, January 1961.

Le Marquis, Antoinette, M.D. "San Diego Medical Practice: A Historical Sketch," *J.A.M.W.A.,* V. 14, No. 6, June 1959.

Lentino, Walter, M.D. in the *Journal of the American Medical Association,* V. 174, No. 12, November 19, 1960.

Lorch, Emil. "The Beaumont House, Its Background and Setting," *The Journal of the Michigan State Medical Society,* Special Beaumont Memorial Number, February 1953.

Lyman, George D., M.D. "The Beginnings of California's Medical History," *California and Western Medicine,* V. 23, pages 561–76, May 1925.

McCormack, Mrs. A. T. "Our Pioneer Heroine of Surgery—Mrs. Jane Todd Crawford," *Filson Club History Quarterly,* V. 6, No. 3, 1932.

Melick, Dermont W. "History of Medicine in Arizona," *Arizona Medicine,* V. 14, pages 26–28, January 1957.

Miller, Lois. "Physician at Hot Springs Recalls Rugged Practice," *Argus-Leader,* Sioux Falls, S.D., March 9, 1952.

Moore, J. T. "Pioneer Doctor's Wife," *Texas State Journal of Medicine,* V. 32, pages 81–84, June 1944.

Moorman, Lewis J., M.D. "Pioneer Medicine in the Southwest," *Bulletin of the History of Medicine,* V. 31, pages 795–810, Sept.–Oct. 1947.

Read, Georgia Willis. "Diseases, Drugs and Doctors on the Oregon-California Trail in the Gold Rush Years," *Missouri Historical Review,* V. 38, No. 3, April 1944.

Reedy, Michael J. "Army Doctors—Pioneers and Pacemakers," *Military Medicine,* December 1961.

Rich, Ezra, M.D. "Early Practice of Medicine and Surgery in Ogden," *Rocky Mountain Medical Journal,* V. 50, pages 23–30, January 1953.

"Sanitary Conditions of Western Steamers," *Iowa Medical Journal,* V. 2, Keokuk, Iowa, 1855.

Schultz, Anne. "Fort Dearborn's Surgeons," *Illinois History,* V. 16, No. 1, October 1862.

Shilton, Earle A. "Gone Under—A Saga of Mountain Men," *The Westerners Brand Book,* Chicago Corral, V. 20, No. 3, May 1963.

Smith, C. A., M.D. "The Medical and Surgical Department of a Railway System," *Texas State Journal of Medicine,* V. 6, 1905.

Stewart, George R. "Prairie Schooner Got Them There," *American Heritage Magazine,* V. 13, pages 4–17, February 1962.

Wesson, Miley B., M.D. "George E. Goodfellow, Frontier Surgeon and Soldier," *Annals Medical History*, New Series, V. 5, No. 3, pages 236–45, May 1933.

Whitmore, W. V. "John Charles Handy, M.D.," *Arizona Medicine*, page 556, December 1956.

BOOKS

Abbott, John S. C. *Christopher Carson, known as Kit Carson*, New York, 1915.

Acheson, Alex W. *Texas Quackery*, Denison, Tex., 1885.

Arnold, Oren. *Thunder in the Southwest; echoes from the wild frontier*, Norman, Okla., 1952.

Atkinson, Donald T. *Magic, Myth and Medicine*, Cleveland, 1956.

Balch, Henry W., M.D. *The Seamen's Medical Guide*, Boston, 1851.

Ball, Charles D., M.D. *Orange County Medical History*, Santa Ana, Calif., 1926.

Bancroft, H. H. *The History of the Northwest Coast*, V. 1, San Francisco, 1886.

Bancroft, H. H. *History of the Pacific States*, San Francisco, 1885.

Barker, B. B. *Letters of Dr. John McLoughlin*, Portland, Ore., 1948.

Barkley, A. H. *Kentucky's Pioneer Lithotomists*, Cincinnati, 1913.

Bay, J. Christian. "Dr. Daniel Drake, 1785–1852" in *Fortune of Books*, Chicago, 1941.

Beaumont, William. *Experiments and Observations on the Gastric Juice and the Physiology of Digestion*, Plattsburg, N.Y., 1833.

Bettmann, Otto L. *A Pictorial History of Medicine*, Springfield, Ill., 1956.

Blackwelder, Bernice. *Great Westerner, the Story of Kit Carson*, Caldwell, Idaho, 1962.

Blassingame, Wyatt, and Glendinning, Richard. *Frontier Doctors*, New York, 1963.

Bolton, H. E. *Spanish Exploration in the Southwest, 1542–1706*, New York, 1916.

Bonner, Thomas Neville. *The Kansas Doctor; A Century of Pioneering*, Lawrence, Kans., 1959.

Bonner, Thomas Neville. *Medicine in Chicago, 1850–1950*, Madison, Wis., 1957.

Brewerton, George D. *Overland with Kit Carson*, New York, 1930.

Bruff, J. Goldsborough. *Gold Rush Journals*, edited by Georgia Willis Read and Ruth Gaines, New York, 1944.

Buley, Roscoe Carlyle. *The Old Northwest Pioneer Period, 1815–1840*, Bloomington, Ind., 1962.

Burns, Walter Noble. *Tombstone*, New York, 1927.

Burr, C. B., M.D. *Medical History of Michigan*, Minneapolis, 1930.

Calder, Ritchie, *Medicine and Man*, London, 1958.

Chambers, J. S. *The Conquest of Cholera*, New York, 1938.

Chittenden, Hiram Martin, *History of Early Steamboat Navigation on the Missouri River*, V. 1, New York, 1903.

Clapesattle, Helen, *The Doctors Mayo*, Garden City, N.Y., 1943.

Cleland, R. G. *The Cattle on a Thousand Hills: Southern California, 1850–1880*, San Marino, Calif., 1951.

Coe, Urling C., M.D. *Frontier Doctor*, New York, 1939.

Connelley, W. E. "Medicine" in *Standard History of Kansas and Kansans*, Lawrence, Kansas, 1918.

Cornell, W. M. *The Ship and Shore Physician and Surgeon*, Boston, 1858.

Cranfill, J. B., M.D. *Dr. J. B. Cranfill's Chronicle: a story of life in Texas, written by himself about himself*, New York, 1916.

Crumbine, Samuel J., M.D. *Frontier Doctor*, Philadelphia, 1949.

Dale, Harrison Clifford. *The Ashley-Smith Explorations and the Discovery of a Central Route to the Pacific, 1822–1829, with the original journals*, edited by Harrison Clifford Dale, Cleveland, 1918.

Dana, Richard Henry. *Two Years before the Mast*, New York, 1884.

Drake, Daniel, M.D. *Pioneer Life in Kentucky*, Cincinnati, 1870.

Drake, Daniel, M.D. *A Systematic Treatise, Historical, Etiological and Practical on the Principal Diseases of the Interior Valley of North America As They Appear in the Caucasian, African, Indian and Esquimaux Varieties of its Population*, Cincinnati, 1850.

Drury, C. M. *Marcus Whitman, M.D., Pioneer and Martyr*, Caldwell, Idaho, 1937.

Dunlop, Richard. "Saddlebag Docs" in *This Is the West*, edited by Robert West Howard, Chicago, 1957.

Duvall, Marius. *A Navy Surgeon in California, 1846–1847*, San Francisco, 1957.

Dye, C. E. *McLoughlin and Old Oregon*, Portland, Ore., 1900.

Estergreen, M. Morgan. *Kit Carson, A Portrait in Courage*, Norman, Okla., 1962.

Evans, John, M.D. *Observations on the Spread of Asiatic Cholera and its Communicable Nature*, Chicago, 1849.

Ficarra, Bernard J. *Essays on Historical Medicine*, New York, 1948.

Flexner, A. *Medical Education in the United States and Canada*, New York, 1910.
Flexner, James. "A Backwoods Galahad: Ephraim McDowell" in *Great Adventures in Medicine*, edited by Samuel B. Rapport and Helen Wright, New York, 1961.
Flexner, James. *Doctors on Horseback*, New York, 1939.
Flint, Timothy. *Recollections of the Last Ten Years Passed in Occasional Residences and Journeyings in the Valley of the Mississippi*, Boston, 1826.
Folsom, James, Ship's Druggist. *The Mariner's Medical Guide*, Boston, 1864.
Fowle, Otto. *Sault Ste. Marie and its Great Waterway*, New York, 1925.
Fox, Genevieve. *Army Surgeon*, Boston, 1944.
Fuller, G. W. *A History of the Pacific Northwest*, New York, 1946.
Gardiner, Charles Fox, M.D. *Doctor at Timberline*, Caldwell, Idaho, 1938.
Garrison, Fielding H. "Contribution of the West to American Medicine" in *Lectures on the History of Medicine*, Philadelphia, 1933.
Geumlek, Lois. "The Doctor and the Skeleton" in *These to Remember*, Centennial Edition, Idaho Poets and Writers Guild, 1962.
Gibson, John M. *Physician to the World, the Life of General William C. Gorgas*, Durham, N.C., 1950.
Gibson, John M. *Soldier in White; the Life of General George Miller Sternberg*, Durham, N.C., 1958.
Gorgas, Marie D. *William Crawford Gorgas; His Life and Work*, Garden City, N.Y., 1935.
Gould, D. F. *Beyond the Shining Mountains*, Portland, Ore., 1938.
Grassick, J., M.D. *North Dakota Medicine, Sketches and Abstracts*, Grand Forks, N.D., 1926.
Gray, W. H. *A History of Oregon*, Portland, Ore., 1870.
Griffin, John S., M.D. *A Doctor Comes to California, the Diary of John S. Griffin, Assistant Surgeon with Kearney's Dragoons, 1846–1847*, Special Publication No. 18, California Historical Society, San Francisco, 1943.
Grinnell, George B. *The Fighting Cheyennes*, Norman, Okla., 1956.
Gross, S. D. "Ephraim McDowell" in *Lives of Eminent American Physicians and Surgeons of the Nineteenth Century*, Philadelphia, 1861.
Guthrie, Douglas. *A History of Medicine*, London, 1945.
Hanson, Joseph M. *The Conquest of the Missouri*, New York, 1909.

Harris, Henry, M.D. *California's Medical Story*, San Francisco, 1932.

Hatcher, Harlan. *The Great Lakes*, New York, 1944.

Havighurst, Walter. *Upper Mississippi; A Wilderness Saga*, New York, 1937.

Hertzler, Arthur E., M.D. *The Horse and Buggy Doctor*, New York, 1938.

Holbrook, Stewart. *Wyatt Earp, U. S. Marshal*, New York, 1956.

Hoover, Herbert. *The Memoirs of Herbert Hoover*, New York, 1952.

Horine, Emmet Field, M.D. *Daniel Drake, Pioneer Physician of the Mid-West*, Philadelphia, 1961.

Hoyt, Henry F. *A Frontier Doctor*, Boston, 1929.

Hume, Edgar Erskine. *Victories of Army Medicine; Scientific Accomplishments of the United States Army*, Philadelphia, 1943.

Hunter, Louis C. *Steamboats on the Western Rivers*, Cambridge, Mass., 1949.

Hussey, John A. *The History of Fort Vancouver*, Portland, Ore., 1957.

Jirka, Frank J. *American Doctors of Destiny*, Chicago, 1940.

Jones, Joseph Roy. *Memories, Men and Medicine*, Sacramento, Calif., 1950.

Jones, Nard. *The Great Command*, Boston, 1959.

Juettner, Otto, M.D. *Daniel Drake and His Followers, 1785–1909; Historical and Biographical Sketches*, Cincinnati, 1909.

Keating, William H. *Narrative of an Expedition to the Sources of St. Peter's River, Lake Winnepeek, Lake of the Woods, etc., performed in the Year 1823, by order of the Hon. J. C. Calhoun, Secretary of War, under the command of Stephen H. Long, Major*, London, 1825.

Kelly, Howard A., M.D. *Walter Reed and Yellow Fever*, Baltimore, 1923.

Kimball, Maria Brace. *A Soldier Doctor of Our Army*, Boston, 1917.

King, Willis P., M.D. *Stories of a Country Doctor*, Philadelphia, 1891.

Kober, George Martin, M.D. *Reminiscences of George Martin Kober, M.D.*, Washington, D.C., 1930.

Kress, George H., M.D. *A History of the Medical Profession of Southern California with an Historical Sketch*, Los Angeles, 1910.

Larsell, O. *The Doctor in Oregon: A Medical History*, Portland, Ore., 1947.

Lee, Nelson. *Three Years among the Comanches*, Albany, N.Y., 1859.

Lewis, Oscar. *Sea Routes to the Gold Fields*, New York, 1949.

Lloyd's Steamboat Directory and Disasters on the Western Waters, Cincinnati, 1856.

Long, Francis A., M.D. *A Prairie Doctor of the 80's*, Norfolk, Nebr., 1938.

Major, Ralph H., M.D. *A History of Medicine*, Springfield, Ill., 1954.

Mansfield, Edward D. *Memoirs of the Life and Services of Daniel Drake, M.D.*, Cincinnati, 1855.

Martin, Douglas D. *Tombstone's Epitaph*, Albuquerque, N.M., 1951.

Martineau, Harriet. *Western Travel*, New York, 1838.

McGillycuddy, Julia E. *McGillycuddy, Agent; a biography of Dr. Valentine T. McGillycuddy*, Stanford, Calif., 1941.

McMechen, Edgar C. *Life of Governor Evans, second territorial governor of Colorado*, Denver, 1924.

Mencken, August. *First Class Passengers*, New York, 1938.

Montgomery, Elizabeth Rider. *The Story behind Great Medical Discoveries*, New York, 1945.

Montgomery, Richard G. *The White-Headed Eagle*, New York, 1935.

Moore, Nathaniel Fisk. *Diary; a trip from New York to the Falls of St. Anthony in 1845*, edited by Stanley Pargelis and Ruth Lapham Butler, Chicago, 1946.

Moorman, Lewis J., M.D. *Pioneer Doctor*, Norman, Okla., 1951.

Morgan, Dale L. *Jedediah Smith and the Opening of the West*, Indianapolis, 1953.

Mowry, William A. *Marcus Whitman and the Early Days of Oregon*, New York, 1901.

Myer, Jesse S., M.D. *Life and Letters of Dr. William Beaumont*, St. Louis, 1912.

Neilson, William P. *The Doctor Was Here, a Saga of Medicine Development as Seen in the Cherokee Outlet*, Guthrie, Okla., No Date.

Nixon, Patrick Ireland, M.D. *A Century of Medicine in San Antonio*, San Antonio, Texas, 1936.

Nixon, Pat Ireland, M.D. *A History of the Texas Medical Association, 1853–1953*, Austin, Tex., 1953.

Nixon, Pat Ireland, M.D. *The Medical Story of Early Texas, 1528–1853*, Lancaster, Pa., 1946.

O'Meara, Walter. *The Savage Trader*, Boston, 1960.

Orr, H. Winnett, M.D. *History of Medicine in Nebraska*, Lincoln, Nebr., 1952.

Packard, Francis R., M.D. *History of Medicine in the U.S.*, New York, 1931.

Parsons, Usher. *Physician for Ships; containing medical advice for seamen and other persons at sea,* Boston, 1851.

Peterson, Frederick W., M.D. *Desert Pioneer Doctor,* Calexico, Calif., 1947.

Phillips, Paul D. *Medicine in the Making of Montana,* Missoula, Mont., 1962.

Pickard, Madge E. and Buley, R. Carlyle. "Dr. Richard Carter" in *Great Adventures in Medicine,* edited by Samuel Rapport and Helen Wright, New York, 1952.

Pickard, Madge E. and Buley, R. Carlyle. *The Midwest Pioneer, His Ills, Cures and Doctors,* New York, 1946.

Porter, Pierre, R., M.D. *Portrait of a Pioneer Physician,* Columbia, Mo., 1943.

Pusey, William Allen, M.D. *High Lights in the History of Chicago Medicine,* Chicago, 1940.

Pusey, William Allen, M.D. *Giants of Medicine in Pioneer Kentucky,* New York, 1938.

Quaife, Milo Milton. *The Southwestern Expedition of Zebulon M. Pike,* edited by Milo Milton Quaife, Chicago, 1925.

Red, Mrs. George Plunkett. *The Medicine Man in Texas,* Houston, 1930.

Reynolds, H. M. *Gold, Rawhide and Iron,* Palo Alto, Calif., 1955.

Ridenbaugh, Mary Young. *The Biography of Ephraim McDowell, M.D.,* New York, 1890.

Riesenberg, Felix. *Cape Horn,* New York, 1939.

Robinson, Victor, M.D. *The Story of Medicine,* New York, 1936.

Rosen, George and Caspari-Rosen, Beate. 400 *Years of a Doctor's Life,* New York, 1947.

Ross, Alexander. *The Fur Hunters of the Far West,* Norman, Okla., 1956.

Rucker, Marvin Pierce. *The Selected Writings of Marvin Pierce Rucker,* Richmond, Va., 1958.

Schachner, A. *Ephraim McDowell, Father of Ovariotomy,* Philadelphia, 1921.

Scott, Walter Dill. *John Evans, an Appreciation,* Evanston, Ill., 1939.

Selleck, Henry B. *Beaumont and the Mackinack Island Miracle,* East Lansing, Mich., 1961.

Sherwell, Samuel, M.D. *Old Recollections of an Old Boy,* New York, 1923.

Sigerist, Henry E. *American Medicine,* New York, 1934.

Smythe, W. E. *History of San Diego,* Chicago, 1924.

Sonnichsen, C. L. *Billy King's Tombstone,* Caldwell, Idaho, 1951.

Stephens, I. K. *The Hermit Philosopher of Liendo*, Dallas, 1951.
Sternberg, Mrs. Martha L. *George Miller Sternberg*, Chicago, 1920.
Thwaites, R. G. *Early Western Travels*, Cleveland, 1905.
Tobey, James A. *Riders of the Plagues*, New York, 1930.
Twain, Mark. *Life on the Mississippi*, Boston, 1883.
Tyson, James L., M.D. *Diary of a Physician in California*, New York, 1850.
Vestal, Stanley. *Kit Carson, the Happy Warrior of the Old West*, Boston, 1928.
Vestal, Stanley. *Mountain Men*, Boston, 1937.
Vogel, Karl. "Medicine at Sea in the Days of Sail" in *Great Adventures in Medicine*, edited by Samuel Rapport and Helen Wright, New York, 1952.
Warman, Cy. *The Story of the Railroad*, New York, 1898.
Webb, Gerald B. and Powell, Desmond. *Henry Sewall—Physiologist and Physician*, Baltimore, 1946.
Wistar, Isaac Jones. *Autobiography of Isaac Jones Wistar, 1827–1905*, Philadelphia, 1914.

INDEX